Keys to Spelling Mastery

Ruel A. Allred

Louise O. Baird

Edwin A. Read

Harold B. Allen, Linguistic Consultant

THE ECONOMY COMPANY

Oklahoma City   Indianapolis   Los Angeles

DESIGN, ART DIRECTION, AND PRODUCTION
James Stockton and Associates
James Stockton
Karen Tucker
Cheryl Carrington

ACKNOWLEDGMENTS
Harcourt Brace Jovanovich, Inc.: For some material
adapted from *The HBJ School Dictionary*, copyright © 1977,
1972, 1968 by Harcourt Brace Jovanovich, Inc. Reprinted
by permission of the publisher.
Illustrators: S. Balestra, Ellen Blonder, Liz Callen, Eileen
Christelow, Lynn Dennis, April Funcke, Susan Gilmour,
Pat Maloney, Ellen Ng, Wendy Nordström, Hank Osuna,
Barbara Reinertson, Steve Reoutt, Roni Shepherd, Dalia
Sudavicius, Judy Sutton, Ed Taber
Photos: © Dan Budnik/Woodfin Camp & Associates 18
(top), 20 (bottom); © Timothy Eagan/Woodfin Camp &
Associates 21; © Shelly Grossman/Woodfin Camp &
Associates 145; © George Hall/Woodfin Camp &
Associates 28; Peter Henricks cover, 43, 71; © Dan Morrill
33 (left); © Norman Prince 33 (right, courtesy of Marine
World/Africa USA, Redwood City, CA), 46, 50, 54, 62,
63, 66, 84, 86, 90, 92, 97, 105, 109; © Alex Webb/Magnum
18 (bottom); © H. Wilks/Stock, Boston 20 (top); © Frank
Wing/Stock, Boston 143; © Cary Wolinsky/Stock, Boston
102

INSTRUCTIONAL CONSULTANTS
Thomas Y. Lee
Patricia L. Smith
Salud Salinda
Marie Grace Molloy, S.P.
Thomas A. Soudelier
Sister Marie Rosarine, S.S.J.
Deb Cates
Carolyn A. Mynatt

The Economy Company,
Educational Publishers
1901 North Walnut
Oklahoma City, Oklahoma   73125
ISBN 0-8332-1505-1

Contents

INTRODUCTION

What Is Spelling?

The letters of the alphabet are used to spell words. Spelling a word correctly means saying or writing the right letters in the right order. Read the following sentences:

1. I wear my kote in the winter.   **2. I wear my atco in the winter.**
3. I wear my coat in the winter.

Underline the sentence above in which the word **coat** is spelled correctly. The word **coat** is spelled correctly in the third sentence. The right letters are in the right order.

A. The words shown in the box below are misspelled in the sentences. Find the misspelled words in the sentences. Write the words correctly. The first one has been done for you.

cat	come	make	me	out

1. Ann has a kat named Sunshine.   cat

2. Will you take mee to the zoo?   _____

3. I saw Sam's bird fly owt the window.   _____

4. Please kum to my house.   _____

5. Help me mak the cake.   _____

B. Write these letters in the right order to form the words shown in the box above.

1. uot   2. akem   3. em   4. atc   5. ecom

_____   _____   _____   _____   _____

4

The Alphabet

A. The alphabet has twenty-six letters. The letters of the alphabet can be written as capital letters or as lowercase letters. Circle the capital letters in the alphabet below. Underline the lowercase letters.

A a   B b   C c   D d   E e   F f   G g   H h   I i   J j   K k   L l   M m

N n   O o   P p   Q q   R r   S s   T t   U u   V v   W w   X x   Y y   Z z

B. Beside each capital letter below write the correct lowercase letter. Beside each lowercase letter write the correct capital letter. The first two have been done for you.

1. E e̲   2. a A̲   3. U ____   4. Z ____

5. j ____   6. o ____   7. t ____   8. D ____

9. y ____   10. i ____   11. n ____   12. S ____

13. X ____   14. c ____   15. H ____   16. M ____

C. The letters of the alphabet are in a certain order called **alphabetical order.** Write the lowercase letter that follows each letter listed below. Look at the alphabet at the top of the page if you need help. The first one has been done for you.

1. e f̲   2. j ____   3. p ____   4. f ____

5. a ____   6. u ____   7. v ____   8. k ____

9. q ____   10. o ____   11. i ____   12. n ____

13. s ____   14. x ____   15. h ____   16. m ____

Handwriting

Write words neatly so that other people can read them. Words may look misspelled if they have not been written neatly.

A. When you write, be sure that you make all the letters touch the bottom line. Write correctly the words shown below.

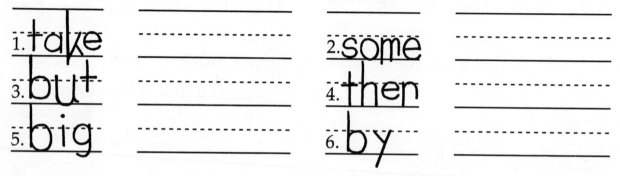

1. take
2. some
3. but
4. then
5. big
6. by

B. When you write, leave the right amount of space between letters. Write each word below. Leave the right amount of space between the letters.

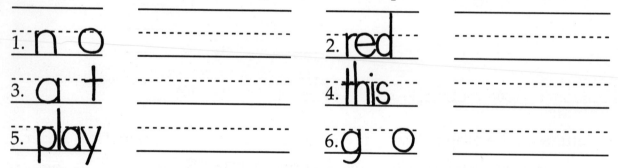

1. n o
2. red
3. a t
4. this
5. play
6. g o

C. When you write, make the letters as tall as they should be. Circle the words below in which the letters are as tall as they should be. Write the words correctly.

1. look
   day
2. look
   day

Long Vowel Sounds

Each letter of the alphabet stands for one or more sounds. The vowel letters **a, e, i, o,** and **u** can stand for the long vowel sounds. The long vowel sounds that the letters stand for are the same as the names of the vowel letters. The symbols that stand for the long vowel sounds are shown below. Read the example words that have the sounds.

/ā/ **cake**　　/ē/ **bean**　　/ī/ **pie**　　/ō/ **rope**　　/ū/ **use**

A. Draw a line under each picture whose name has a long vowel sound.

1. 　　2. 　　3.

B. Read the words below. In each row circle the words that have the vowel sound that the symbol stands for.

/ā/	1. cat	2. ate	3. wait	4. play	5. brave
/ē/	1. eat	2. bed	3. tree	4. seat	5. deep
/ī/	1. like	2. bite	3. big	4. high	5. ice
/ō/	1. block	2. coat	3. note	4. know	5. so
/ū/	1. cue	2. cute	3. huge	4. fuse	5. bus

C. Read the words below. In each pair of words underline the word that has a long vowel sound.

1. rip　ripe　　　　2. plane　plan　　　　3. cub　cube
4. feed　fed　　　　5. rode　rod

Short Vowel Sounds

The vowel letters **a, e, i, o,** and **u** can stand for the long vowel sounds. The vowel letters also can stand for the short vowel sounds.

The symbols that stand for the short vowel sounds are shown below. Read the example words that have the sounds.

/ă/ **hat**   /ě/ **pet**   /ĭ/ **pig**   /ŏ/ **top**   /ŭ/ **nut**

A. Draw a line under each picture whose name has a short vowel sound.

1.    2.    3.

B. Read the words below. In each row circle the words that have the vowel sound that the symbol stands for.

/ă/	1. cat	2. rain	3. back	4. rag	5. act
/ě/	1. bed	2. pen	3. bend	4. cent	5. clean
/ĭ/	1. pie	2. fish	3. trip	4. pin	5. bit
/ŏ/	1. box	2. fox	3. road	4. shop	5. not
/ŭ/	1. cup	2. brush	3. but	4. cube	5. rub

C. Read the words below. In each pair of words underline the word that has a short vowel sound.

1. tub   tube   2. fine   fin   3. cute   cut

4. hid   hide   5. lick   like

Long and Short Vowel Sounds

A. Underline the correct answers. The **(long, short)** vowel sounds are the same as the names of the vowel letters. The symbols /ā/, /ē/, /ī/, /ō/, and /ū/ stand for the **(long, short)** vowel sounds. The symbols /ă/, /ĕ/, /ĭ/, /ŏ/, and /ŭ/ stand for the **(long, short)** vowel sounds.

B. Write the words from the box beside the correct symbols.

add	
be	
bent	
blow	
brick	
bright	
brush	
came	
clock	
use	

1. /ā/ _____   2. /ē/ _____

3. /ī/ _____   4. /ō/ _____

5. /ū/ _____   6. /ă/ _____

7. /ĕ/ _____   8. /ĭ/ _____

9. /ŏ/ _____   10. /ŭ/ _____

C. The names of Jean's favorite animals have long vowel sounds. The names of Bill's favorite animals have short vowel sounds. Write these animal names on the correct posters below: **cat, duck, fox, goat, hen, mice, mule, pig, sheep, whale.**

My Favorite Animals by Jean

1. _____   2. _____

3. _____   4. _____

5. _____

My Favorite Animals by Bill

1. _____   2. _____

3. _____   4. _____

5. _____

Consonant Sounds

The letters **a, e, i, o,** and **u** are vowel letters and can stand for the long and short vowel sounds. All the other letters of the alphabet are consonant letters. Each consonant letter stands for one or more consonant sounds.

A. Name the pictures below. Circle the pictures whose names begin with the same sound as **move.**

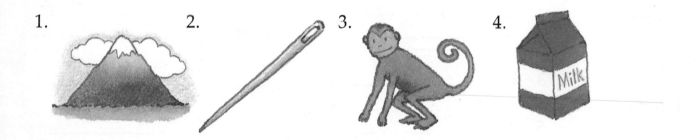

1.   2.   3.   4.

B. Read the word and name the pictures in each row below. Circle the pictures whose names end with the same sound as the word.

1. can   a.   b.   c.   d.

2. dog   a.   b.   c.   d.

Consonant Sounds

A. Double consonant letters sometimes stand for one consonant sound. Name each picture. Circle the double consonant letters that stand for the sound you hear at the end of the picture name.

1. nn gg ll 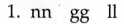   2. ss pp tt 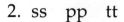   3. zz ss ff 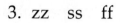   4. mm bb gg

B. Sometimes two or more consonant letters stand for sounds that are heard together, such as **pl** in **play.** Draw lines to match the pictures whose names begin with the same sounds.

1.    2.

3.    4.

C. Sometimes two consonant letters stand for one consonant sound, such as **sh** in **sheep.** Underline the pictures whose names begin with the same sound.

1.   2.   3.   4.

The Eight Study Steps

You can use the Eight Study Steps to learn how to spell any word. The pictures on these pages show you how to use the Eight Study Steps to learn how to spell **above.**

a-b-o-v-e

above

a-b-o-v-e

a   bove

1. Say the word.

2. Look carefully at each part of the word.

3. Say the letters in the word.

4. Close your eyes and spell the word.

above

above

above

above

5. Check the word to see whether you have spelled it correctly.

6. Write the word.

7. Check the word to see whether you have written it correctly.

8. If you misspelled the word, repeat the seven steps.

Use the Eight Study Steps to learn how to spell **front.** Write the

word here. _____

Use the Eight Study Steps to learn how to spell **maybe.** Write the

word here. _____

am	at	can	had	ran
as	and	cat	man	**have**

Spelling Clues

Say each list word. Follow the directions.

A. Write the list words in which the short vowel sound /ă/ as heard in **hat** is the first sound.

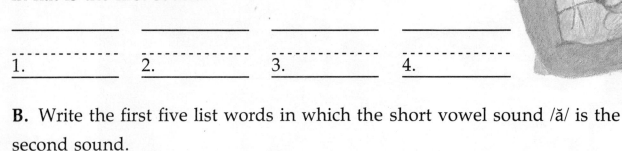

1. _____   2. _____   3. _____   4. _____

B. Write the first five list words in which the short vowel sound /ă/ is the second sound.

1. _____   2. _____   3. _____   4. _____   5. _____

C. In each word you wrote, circle the letter that stands for the short vowel sound /ă/.

The short vowel sound /ă/ is usually spelled **a** as in **man**.

Watch Out!   Write the list word that has the short vowel sound /ă/ and ends

_____

with silent **e.** _____
Take the Pretest.

Practice

A. Write the list words shown in the box to complete the sentences. The first one has been done for you.

am	and	as	at	can

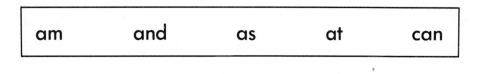

1. Today I ___am___ going to a fair.

2. My brother _____ sister are going, too.

3. We will go _____ soon as Mom gets home from work.

4. Do you think you _____ go, too?

5. I know we can have fun _____ the fair.

B. Write the list words shown in the box in the correct word shapes. The first one has been done for you.

cat	had	have	man	ran

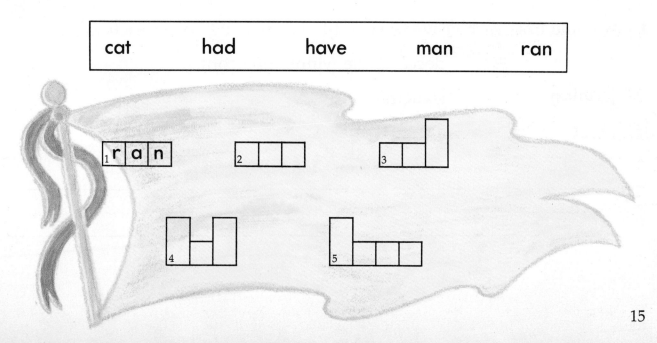

1. r a n

Take the Check Test. Write on your Study Sheet the words you misspell.

Dictionary

A. Complete the alphabet. Write the letters that are missing.

b   d   h

| n   r

t   v   w   z

B. Write the sets of letters below in alphabetical order. The first set has been done for you.

1. e   d   c   f

c   d   e   f

2. r   q   p   o

3. j   m   l   k

4. u   v   t   s

Spelling Challenge

fair   judging   prize   I

Draw a line from each challenge word to its meaning. Write each word.

1. fair   deciding the winner of a contest

2. judging   something that is won

3. prize   a festival

4. I   a word used when talking about yourself

1.   2.   3.   4.

Written Expression

A. The seven days of the week are in a certain order. The names of the days of the week are always capitalized. Underline the names of the days of the week below. The first one has been done for you.

<u>Sunday</u> is the first day of the week. Then come Monday, Tuesday, Wednesday, Thursday, Friday, and Saturday.

B. Read the sentences. Write the names of the days of the week in the correct order. The first one has been done for you.

1. Tom had a party on ___Sunday___ .

2. On _____ morning Dee ran to catch the bus.

3. On _____ a man came to fix our television.

4. Mary's cat had kittens on _____ .

5. I baked an apple pie on _____ .

6. I stayed at Grandfather's on _____ .

7. Dad and I went to the fair on _____ .

C. Complete the sentence.

_____ is the best day of the week.

Take the Final Test.

bed   let   red   ten   **said**

get   men   set   yes   **says**

Spelling Clues

Say each list word. Follow the directions.

A. Write the list words that have the letter **e.**

1. _____ 2. _____ 3. _____ 4. _____

5. _____ 6. _____ 7. _____ 8. _____

B. Underline the correct answer. The vowel sound in each word you wrote above is called a **(long, short)** vowel sound.

C. Underline the letter that stands for the short vowel sound /ĕ/ as heard in **pet** in each word you wrote.

> The short vowel sound /ĕ/ is usually spelled **e** as in **bed.**

Watch Out! Write the list words in which the short vowel sound /ĕ/ is not spelled **e.**

1. _____ 2. _____

Take the Pretest.

Practice

A. Write a list word from the box to name each picture.

bed	men	red	ten

1. _____ 2. _____ 3. _____ 4. _____

B. Write the list words that rhyme with **met.**

1. _____

2. _____

3. _____

_____

C. Write the list word that means the opposite of **no.** _____

D. Write **said** or **says** to complete the sentences.

1. Dad _____ yesterday that we could go
to the museum.

2. This sign _____ the museum
opens at ten o'clock.

Take the Check Test. Write on your Study Sheet the words you misspell.

Dictionary

Write each set of letters in alphabetical order.

1. **d v o i**
_____
- - - - - - - - - - - - - -
_____

3. **f x t s**
_____
- - - - - - - - - - - - - -

5. **g l b k**
_____
- - - - - - - - - - - - - -

7. **u e a o i**
_____
- - - - - - - - - - - - - -
_____

2. **e p a q**
_____
- - - - - - - - - - - - - -

4. **w c m h**
_____
- - - - - - - - - - - - - -

6. **j z r n**
_____
- - - - - - - - - - - - - -
_____

Spelling Challenge

art museums visitor <u>had</u>

Write the correct challenge words to complete the sentences.

_____
- - - - - - - - - - - - - -

1. I _____ never been to a museum until today.

_____
- - - - - - - - - - - - - -

2. Today I was a _____ at the Museum of Modern Art.

_____
- - - - - - - - - - - - - -

3. I enjoyed looking at the great works of _____ .

_____
- - - - - - - - - - - - - -

4. I would like to visit other _____ .

Written Expression

A. Read the names of the months of the year: **January, February, March, April, May, June, July, August, September, October, November, December.** Underline the correct answer. The name of each month begins with a **(capital letter, lowercase letter).**

Read this sentence: **Dean was born on October 11, 1973.** Underline the correct answer. The punctuation mark that is between the day of the month and the year in the date **October 11, 1973,** is a **(comma, period, question mark).**

B. Copy these dates correctly.

1. March 10, 1976 _____

2. August 9, 1970 _____

3. May 4, 1978 _____

C. Read the sentences. Write the dates correctly.

1. The museum opened on january 22 1969. _____

_____

2. Two men walked on the moon on july 20 1969. _____

_____

D. Complete the sentence by writing the correct date.

I was born on _____ .

Take the Final Test.

LESSON 3 A Spelling of /ĭ/

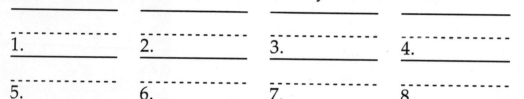

if	is	big	pig	<u>been</u>
in	it	hit	sit	<u>give</u>

Spelling Clues

Say each list word. Follow the directions.

A. Write the list words that have only one vowel letter.

1. _____ 2. _____ 3. _____ 4. _____

5. _____ 6. _____ 7. _____ 8. _____

B. Underline the correct answer. The vowel sound in each word you wrote above is called a **(long, short)** vowel sound.

C. Circle the letter that stands for the short vowel sound /ĭ/ as heard in **pig** in each word you wrote above.

> The short vowel sound /ĭ/ is usually spelled **i** as in **big.**

Watch Out! Write the list words in which the short vowel sound /ĭ/ is spelled the following ways.

1. **ee** 2. **i** silent **e,** separated by a consonant letter

<u>Take the Pretest.</u>

_____
- - - - - - - - - -
_____
- - - - - - - - - -
_____

Practice

A. Put the letters from the Ferris wheel cars in front of the letters in the center of the wheels. Write the list words that are formed. The first one has been done for you.

1. hit   2. _____   3. _____   4. _____

B. Unscramble and write the Watch Out words.

1. _____

2. _____

C. Write the list word **if.** Change the consonant letter in **if** to form three more list words. Write the three list words.

1. _____   2. _____   3. _____   4. _____

Take the Check Test. Write on your Study Sheet the words you misspell.

Word Building

A. Change the letter **i** in the list words to the letter **a.** Complete the sentences by writing the words that are formed.

1. **hit**—Throw three balls into the _____ .

2. **big**—Win a _____ that is full of surprises.

B. Change the letter **i** in the list words to the letter **e.** Complete the sentences by writing the words that are formed.

1. **big**—That little dog can sit up and _____ .

2. **pig**—Throw a ring over the _____ and win a prize.

Spelling Challenge

carnival   crowds   excitement   said

Complete the poster. Write the correct challenge words in the sentences.

SCHOOL CARNIVAL

1. Do you like _____ of people?

2. Do you like fun and _____ ?

3. Come to the school _____ .

4. It has been _____ that you can have fun there.

Written Expression

A. Copy the sentences. Notice that each sentence begins with a capital letter and ends with a period or a question mark.

1. Have you ever been to a carnival?

2. It is fun to go to carnivals.

3. You can go with me if you would like.

4. I will give you a ticket.

B. Complete the sentence.

At the carnival we can

Take the Final Test.

on	got	hot	lot	top
box	hop	job	not	<u>want</u>

Spelling Clues

Say each list word. Follow the directions.

A. Write the list word in which the short vowel

‾‾‾‾‾‾‾‾‾

- - - - - - - - - - -

sound /ŏ/ as heard in **top** is the first sound. ‾‾‾‾‾‾‾‾‾

B. Write the list words in which the short vowel sound /ŏ/ is the middle sound.

‾‾‾‾‾‾ ‾‾‾‾‾‾ ‾‾‾‾‾‾ ‾‾‾‾‾‾

- - - - - -   - - - - - -   - - - - - -   - - - - - -
1.‾‾‾‾‾ 2.‾‾‾‾‾ 3.‾‾‾‾‾ 4.‾‾‾‾‾

- - - - - -   - - - - - -   - - - - - -   - - - - - -
5.‾‾‾‾‾ 6.‾‾‾‾‾ 7.‾‾‾‾‾ 8.‾‾‾‾‾

C. Circle the letter that stands for the short vowel sound /ŏ/ in each word you wrote above.

> The short vowel sound /ŏ/ is usually spelled **o** as in **box.**

Watch Out! Write the list word in which the short vowel sound /ŏ/ is not

‾‾‾‾‾‾

- - - - - - -

spelled **o.** ‾‾‾‾‾‾
Take the Pretest.

Practice

A. Write these list words to complete the sentences.

box	job	on	want

1. The winner stands on a ____________ .
2. Both players ____________ to win.
3. Five players are ____________ the team.
4. She wants to do a good ____________ .

TEAM
RUTH
JUAN
MARIO
DAVID
LIN

B. Write the list words that rhyme with **cot**.

1. ____________ 2. ____________

3. ____________ 4. ____________

C. Change the consonant letter **m** in **mop** to form two list words. Write the list words.

1. ____________ 2. ____________

Take the Check Test. Write on your Study Sheet the words you misspell.

Dictionary

A. Write the following letters in alphabetical order after the numerals.

t   s   r

1. ___ack   2. ___ack   3. ___ack

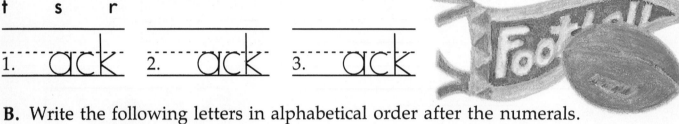

B. Write the following letters in alphabetical order after the numerals.

l   j   b   p

1. ___ack   2. ___ack   3. ___ack   4. ___ack

C. Write the following letters in alphabetical order after the numerals.

h   g   w   j

1. ___ot   2. ___ot   3. ___ob   4. ___ant

D. Read the words above. Underline the correct answers. 1. The words in each activity **(are, are not)** in alphabetical order. 2. The **(first, last)** letter in each word shows that the words are in alphabetical order.

Spelling Challenge

cheer   noise   sports   <u>in</u>

Draw a line from each word to its meaning.
Write the challenge words.

cheer	inside something	_____ _____
in	a yell	1. _____ 2. _____
noise	games or contests	
sports	any sound	3. _____ 4. _____

Review

Read the words in each set. If one of the words is misspelled, fill in the numbered circle beside that word. If none of the words is misspelled, fill in the numbered circle beside the word **None**. The first one has been done for you.

A. ● giv
   ② in
   ③ let
   ④ and
   ⑤ None

B. ① big
   ② on
   ③ seys
   ④ lot
   ⑤ None

C. ① want
   ② sit
   ③ ran
   ④ it
   ⑤ None

D. ① not
   ② box
   ③ hit
   ④ if
   ⑤ None

E. ① at
   ② am
   ③ got
   ④ cat
   ⑤ None

F. ① man
   ② hav
   ③ is
   ④ men
   ⑤ None

G. ① set
   ② yis
   ③ red
   ④ ten
   ⑤ None

H. ① pig
   ② had
   ③ job
   ④ bed
   ⑤ None

I. ① hop
   ② git
   ③ been
   ④ can
   ⑤ None

Take the Final Test.

| up | but | cut | run | <u>of</u> |
| us | cup | fun | sun | <u>was</u> |

Spelling Clues

Say each list word. Follow the directions.

A. Write the list words that have the letter **u.**

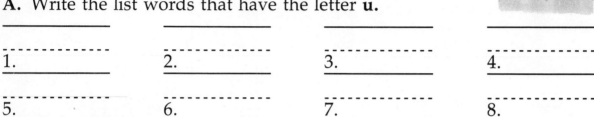

1. _____ 2. _____ 3. _____ 4. _____

5. _____ 6. _____ 7. _____ 8. _____

B. Underline the correct answer. The vowel sound in each word you wrote above is called a **(long, short)** vowel sound.

C. Circle the letter that stands for the short vowel sound /ŭ/ as heard in **nut** in each word you wrote.

> The short vowel sound /ŭ/ is usually spelled **u** as in **fun.**

Watch Out! Write the list words in which the short vowel sound /ŭ/ is not

spelled **u.**   1. _____   2. _____

Take the Pretest.

Practice

A. Write these list words next to their clues: **cup, cut, fun, sun, up.** The first one has been done for you.

1. gives light and heat to the earth _sun_

2. to break up into parts _____

3. play _____

4. not down _____

5. something used for drinking _____

B. Write these list words to complete the sentences: **but, of, run, us, was.**

1. _____

2. _____

3. _____

4. _____

5. _____

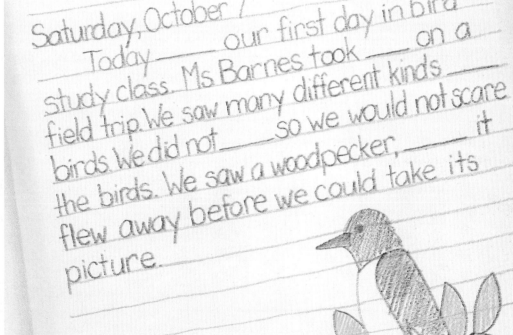

Saturday, October 7
Today ___ our first day in bird study class. Ms Barnes took ___ on a field trip. We saw many different kinds ___ birds. We did not ___ so we would not scare the birds. We saw a woodpecker, ___ it flew away before we could take its picture.

Take the Check Test. Write on your Study Sheet the words you misspell.

Word Building

Change the vowel letters in the words below to form list words. Write the list words. The first one has been done for you.

1. bat but

2. if _____

3. son _____

4. fan _____

5. cat _____

6. ran _____

7. cap _____

8. is _____

Spelling Challenge

grain　　　hummingbird　　　lists　　　*it*

Complete the sentences by writing the correct challenge words.

1. Emma likes bird study because _____ is fun.

2. Emma _____ in a notebook names of birds that she studies.

3. The _____ is her favorite bird.

4. Emma gives seed and _____ to the birds.

Written Expression

A. Read the sentences.

1. We have fun in our bird study class.

2. Would you like to come with us to our class?

Underline the word or words that complete these sentences.

1. At the end of the telling sentence is a **(period, question mark)**.

2. At the end of the asking sentence is a **(period, question mark)**.

B. Read the sentences below. Put a period at the end of each telling sentence. Put a question mark at the end of each asking sentence.

1. Have you seen birds flying high in the sky ___

2. An ostrich can run very fast ___

3. Did you know that the ostrich is the largest of all the birds ___

4. This bird's feathers shine in the sun ___

C. Complete the sentence. Put a period at the end of the sentence.

_____

- -

The _____ is my favorite bird

Take the Final Test.

an	end	hen	his	six
did	has	him	pet	<u>live</u>

Spelling Clues

Say each list word. Follow the directions.

A. Write the list words that have only one vowel letter.

1. _____
2. _____
3. _____

4. _____
5. _____
6. _____

7. _____
8. _____
9. _____

B. Underline the correct answer. The vowel sound in each word you wrote above is called a **(long, short)** vowel sound.

> A short vowel sound is usually spelled with one vowel letter as in **has.**

Watch Out! Write the list word that has two vowel letters. _____
<u>Take the Pretest.</u>

Practice

A. Write the list words that name the pictures.

1. ![six] 2. ![hen]

1. _____
2. _____

B. Unscramble and write the list words. The first one has been done for you.

1. na   **a** **n** _____

2. dne   _____ _____ _____

3. ddi   _____ _____ _____

4. pte

5. hmi   _____ _____ _____

6. hsa   _____ _____ _____

7. sih   _____ _____ _____

8. ilev   _____ _____ _____ _____

Write the letters that are in the boxes above. _____

Unscramble the letters above to find the name of something that many people

_____

collect. Write the name. _____

6

Dictionary

Write each set of words in alphabetical order. One word in each set has been done for you.

1. end   _____
   did   _____
   can   *end*

2. fun   _____
   has   *has*
   get

3. in   *him*
   him   _____
   job   _____

4. pet   *not*
   on   _____
   not   _____

5. ten   _____
   six   _____
   ran   *ten*

6. kite   _____
   joy   *kite*
   live   _____

Spelling Challenge

coin   hobby   postcards   <u>on</u>

Draw a line from each word to its meaning. Write the words.

1. **coin**   a. upon
2. **on**   b. a piece of metal used as money
3. **hobby**   c. cards with pictures on them that can be sent by mail
4. **postcards**   d. something done for pleasure during spare time

1. _____

2. _____

3. _____

4. _____

Written Expression

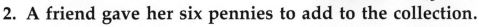

A. Read the sentences.

1. My sister has a coin collection.

2. A friend gave her six pennies to add to the collection.

Underline the correct answer. The first word in each sentence begins with a **(capital letter, lowercase letter).**

B. Rewrite the sentences below. Begin the first word of each sentence with a capital letter.

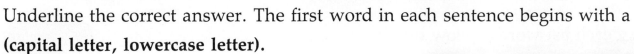

1. did you see this postcard from Glen?

_____

_____

_____

2. on the back he asks me to visit him.

_____

_____

_____

C. Write the following sentence correctly and complete it with your own words: **collecting _____ would be fun because _____ .**

_____

_____

_____

_____

Take the Final Test.

bell	doll	hill	tell	will
bill	fell	sell	well	<u>until</u>

Spelling Clues

Say each list word. Follow the directions.

A. Write the list words that end with **ell** or **oll**.

1. _____ 2. _____ 3. _____

4. _____ 5. _____ 6. _____

B. Write the list words that end with **ill.**

1. _____ 2. _____ 3. _____

C. Underline the correct answer. The vowel sound in each word you wrote above is called a **(long, short)** vowel sound.

D. Underline the letters that stand for the sound /l/ in each word you wrote above.

> The consonant sound /l/ at the end of a word is often spelled **ll** if it follows a short vowel sound as in **well.**

Watch Out! Write the list word in which the sound /l/ is spelled **l**.
Take the Pretest.

_____

Practice

A. Write the list words that are formed by putting the letters that are on the spoons in front of the letters that are on the bowl. The first one has been done for you.

1. bell   2.   3.   4.   5.

B. Write these list words to complete the story below: **bill, doll, hill, until, will.**

"What can I give my sister for her birthday?" Barney asked himself.

"I know. I 1._____ bake a cake for her."

Barney walked up the 2._____ to the grocery store. He

bought some eggs with his crisp new dollar 3._____ . Then he walked home to bake the cake.

Barney made the cake in the shape of a 4._____ . Then he

hid the cake so his sister would not see it 5._____ her birthday.

Take the Check Test. Write on your Study Sheet the words you misspell.

Dictionary

Write each set of words in alphabetical order.

1. will _____
   doll _____
   bell _____

2. sell _____
   hill _____
   until _____

3. bell _____
   tell _____
   fell _____

Spelling Challenge

baking   kitchen

homemade   want

Write the correct challenge words to answer the questions.

1. I am a room in which food is prepared and cooked. What am I?   _____

2. I am a word that means **made at home.** What word am I?   _____

3. I am a word that means **to wish for.** What word am I?   _____

4. I am a word that means **cooking in an oven.** What word am I?   _____

Written Expression

A. Underline the correct answers.

1. The first word of a sentence begins with a **(capital letter, lowercase letter)**.

2. A sentence that tells something can end with a **(comma, period)**.

3. A sentence that asks a question ends with a
(period, question mark).

B. Write the following sentences correctly.

1. **Barney bought eggs with his dollar bill**

_____

_____

2. **he made a doll cake for his sister**

_____

_____

3. **his sister could not see the cake until her birthday**

_____

_____

C. Write this question correctly: **will you please help me cook supper**

_____

_____

Take the Final Test.

best	help	just	milk	next
fast	jump	last	must	went

Spelling Clues

Say each list word. Follow the directions.

A. Write the list words that have the letter **e** followed by two consonant

letters. 1. _____ 2. _____ 3. _____ 4. _____

B. Write the list words that have the letter **a** followed by two consonant

letters. 1. _____ 2. _____

C. Write the list words that have the letter **u** followed by two consonant

letters. 1. _____ 2. _____ 3. _____

D. Write the list word that has the letter **i** followed

by two consonant letters. _____

E. Underline the correct answer. The vowel
sound in each list word is called a **(long, short)** vowel sound.

A short vowel sound is usually spelled with one vowel letter. The vowel
letter is followed by one or more consonant letters as in **milk.**

Take the Pretest.

Practice

A. Write two pairs of list words that rhyme.

_____

1. _____ 2. _____

_____

1. _____ 2. _____

B. Write these list words to complete the sentences below:
best, help, next, went.

_____

1. I _____ to the art store to buy colored pencils.

2. The woman at the store helped me find

_____

the _____ pencils.

_____

3. I will buy paint _____ week.

_____

4. I will ask the woman to _____ me again.

C. Write the list words that go with the pictures.

_____   _____

1. _____   2. _____

43

Take the Check Test. Write on your Study Sheet the words you misspell.

Word Building

A. Read the words. Change the vowel letters to form list words. Write the list words.

1. mast _____ 2. fist _____ 3. want _____

B. Read the words. Change the vowel letters to form the words that name the pictures. Write the new words.

1. wall _____

2. men _____

Spelling Challenge

alone   paintbrush   proud   <u>fun</u>   _____

A. Write the challenge word that names the picture. _____

B. Write the correct challenge words to complete the sentences.

I like to draw when I am 1._____ . I am 2._____ of

the pictures I draw. Drawing is 3._____ .

Written Expression

A. Read each sentence.

1. <u>The girls</u> want to help. 2. <u>The puppy</u> will jump and play.

The underlined part of each sentence tells what or whom the sentence is about.

B. Underline the part of each sentence that tells what or whom the sentence is about. **1. Fay runs fast. 2. My cat likes to drink milk.**

C. Complete the sentences by writing the correct words so that the sentences will tell about the picture.

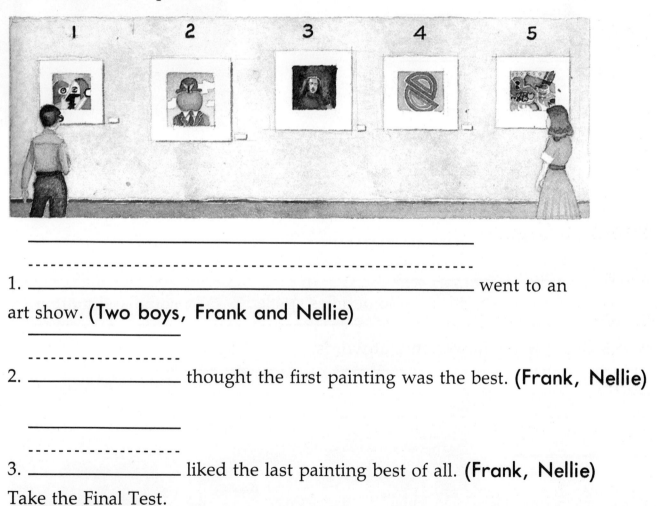

1. _____ went to an art show. **(Two boys, Frank and Nellie)**

2. _____ thought the first painting was the best. **(Frank, Nellie)**

3. _____ liked the last painting best of all. **(Frank, Nellie)**

<u>Take the Final Test.</u>

come	love	money	mother	<u>once</u>
done	some	other	<u>does</u>	<u>color</u>

Spelling Clues

Say each list word. Follow the directions.

A. Write the list words that end with **o** silent **e,** separated by a consonant letter.

1. _____   2. _____

3. _____   4. _____

B. Write the list words that have two vowel sounds.

1. _____   2. _____

3. _____   4. _____

The short vowel sound /ŭ/ is sometimes spelled **o** as in **come** and **mother.**

Watch Out! Write the Watch Out words.

1. _____   2. _____   3. _____

<u>Take the Pretest.</u>

Practice

A. Write the list words from the flowers to complete the story.

_____

1. My _____ and I have a garden in our back yard.

_____

2. We grow roses and _____ flowers there.

_____

3. Our flowers grow in every _____ of the rainbow.

4. Caring for our garden is fun, and it does not cost a lot of

_____

_____ .

color

money

mother

other

B. Draw a line from each scrambled list word to its correct spelling.
The first one has been done for you.

1. meoc	some
2. soed	once
3. doen	does
4. ovel	come
5. enco	love
6. omes	done

Write the correct spellings of the list words above.

1. _____   2. _____   3. _____

4. _____   5. _____   6. _____

Take the Check Test. Write on your Study Sheet the words you misspell.

Dictionary

Write each set of words in alphabetical order.

1. color
   does
   help
   and

2. love
   once
   money
   pet

3. tell
   some
   went
   until

Read the lists of alphabetical words. Circle the correct answer. When the lists are read as one list, the list (is, is not) in alphabetical order.

Spelling Challenge

hoe   tools   vegetable   an

Draw a line from each challenge word to its meaning. Write the words.

1. vegetable   a plant used as food
2. an   things used in work
3. tools   a garden tool
4. hoe   a word used to refer to one of something, as ___ apple

1. _____   2. _____

3. _____   4. _____

Written Expression

A. Read each sentence.

1. Mother <u>went to the gas station</u>.   **2. The boy <u>lost some money</u>.**

The underlined words in each sentence tell what happened in the sentence.

B. Underline the words that tell what happened in each of the following sentences. **1. The cat chased the birds.**   **2. The birds flew away.**

C. Complete the sentences below so that they will tell about the picture.

1. The boy _____

.

(is planting a vegetable garden, likes to eat vegetables)

2. Some birds _____.

(fly over the garden, sit on the ground)

3. The birdhouse _____.

(is in a wagon, is in the tree)

Take the Final Test.

cake	face	gave	make	same
came	game	made	name	take

Spelling Clues

Say each list word. Follow the directions.

A. Write the list words that end with **ame.**

1. _____ 2. _____ 3. _____ 4. _____

B. Write the list words that end with **ake.**

1. _____ 2. _____ 3. _____

C. Write the list words that end with **ace, ave,** and **ade.**

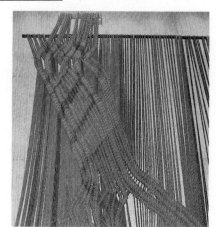

1. _____ 2. _____ 3. _____

D. Underline the correct answer. The long vowel sound /ā/ as heard in **cake** in each list word (**is, is not**) spelled **a** silent **e,** separated by a consonant letter.

The long vowel sound /ā/ is often spelled **a** silent **e,** separated by a consonant letter as in **cake.**

Take the Pretest.

Practice

A. Use the code below to join the list word parts. Write the list words.

g	n	ake	m	c	t	ame	s
1	2	3	4	5	6	7	8

1. 5 + 3 _____

2. 2 + 7 _____

3. 1 + 7 _____

4. 8 + 7 _____

5. 4 + 3 _____

6. 6 + 3 _____

B. Write the list words shown in the box to complete the story.

came	face	gave	made

My friend Betty 1._____ to visit me today. We 2._____

puppets out of paper sacks. I put a funny 3._____ on my puppet.

After Betty went home, I 4._____ my puppet to my brother.

51

Take the Check Test. Write on your Study Sheet the words you misspell.

Word Building

Write the words that are formed by adding the consonant letters to the word parts. The first set has been done for you.

1. n ⎤
   c ⎬ ame
   s ⎦

2. m ⎤
   t ⎬ ake
   c ⎦

3. f ⎤
   n ⎬ ail
   p ⎦

4. g ⎤
   p ⎬ ain
   r ⎦

name
came
same

Spelling Challenge

able   gift   leather   his

Write the correct challenge words to complete the sentences.

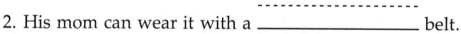

1. Paul is making a sweater for _____ mom.

2. His mom can wear it with a _____ belt.

3. It will be a nice _____ for her.

4. Will Paul be _____ to finish it in time?

Review

Read the words in each set. If one of the words is misspelled, fill in the numbered circle beside that word. If none of the words is misspelled, fill in the numbered circle beside **none of these.** The first one has been done for you.

A. ① best
    ② up
    ● fas
    ④ but
    ⑤ none of these

B. ① money
    ② sell
    ③ of
    ④ hlp
    ⑤ none of these

C. ① hen
    ② coler
    ③ pet
    ④ fell
    ⑤ none of these

D. ① just
    ② run
    ③ whent
    ④ end
    ⑤ none of these

E. ① came
    ② sun
    ③ some
    ④ last
    ⑤ none of these

F. ① jump
    ② other
    ③ make
    ④ an
    ⑤ none of these

G. ① mothir
    ② bell
    ③ made
    ④ fun
    ⑤ none of these

H. ① wus
    ② six
    ③ has
    ④ did
    ⑤ none of these

I. ① hil
    ② next
    ③ name
    ④ will
    ⑤ none of these

Take the Final Test.

fine	home	kite	nice	rope
five	hope	like	ride	time

Spelling Clues

Say each list word. Follow the directions.

A. Write the list words.

1. _____
2. _____
3. _____

4. _____
5. _____
6. _____

7. _____
8. _____

9. _____
10. _____

B. Underline the correct answers. 1. The sound that the first vowel letter stands for in each list word is called a **(long, short)** vowel sound. 2. The silent letter at the end of each list word is a **(vowel, consonant)** letter. 3. The first vowel letter and silent **e** are separated by a **(vowel, consonant)** letter.

C. Write the numeral **2** by the kind of letter found second in the list words. Write the numeral **3** by the kind of letter found third. Write the numeral **4** by the kind of letter found last in the list words.

_____ silent **e** _____ vowel with long sound _____ consonant

> A long vowel sound is often spelled with one vowel letter and silent **e,** separated by a consonant letter as in **fine** and **hope.**

Take the Pretest.

Practice

A. Write these list words to complete the story.

five   home   like   nice   time

I had a good 1. _____ last night. My sister and her band let

me listen while they practiced in our 2. _____ . They practiced

for 3. _____ hours. They played 4. _____ music. I told

them I would 5. _____ to hear them play again.

B. Write each list word in the correct word shape.

fine   kite   ride

1. _____   2. _____   3. _____

C. Unscramble and write these list words.

1. _____

2. _____

Take the Check Test. Write on your Study Sheet the words you misspell.

Dictionary

A **dictionary** is a book that tells meanings of words, either in pictures or in words.

Each word listed in a dictionary is called an **entry word.**

Write the correct entry words beside the picture definitions.

> rope   kite   man   red

1. _____

2. _____

3. _____

4. _____

Spelling Challenge

bow   harp   tunes   un<u>til</u>

Write the correct challenge words to complete the sentences.

1. A _____ is played by plucking it with the fingers.

2. A violin is played by drawing a _____ across its strings.

3. Musicians practice a. _____ they can play b. _____ well.

Written Expression

A. Complete each sentence below with one of the following word groups so that the sentence tells about the picture.

walks in front   play in a band   like the parade

1. Five friends _____ .

2. The band leader _____ .

3. The boys _____ .

B. Complete the sentence.

If I could be in a band, I would play _____ because

_____ .

Take the Final Test.

be	go	me	she	we
by	he	my	so	<u>see</u>

Spelling Clues

Say each list word. Follow the directions.

A. Write the first nine list words.

1.	2.	3.
4.	5.	6.
7.	8.	9.

B. Underline the correct answers. 1. The sound that the vowel letter stands for in each list word you wrote is called a **(long, short)** vowel sound. 2. Each word you wrote begins with one or more **(vowel, consonant)** letters. 3. The number of vowel letters at the end of each word you wrote is **(one, two)**.

C. Circle the letters below that you see at the end of the list words you wrote.

a   e   i   o   u   y

> A long vowel sound at the end of a short word is often spelled with one vowel letter or **y** as in **be, go,** and **my.**

Watch Out! Write the list word in which the long vowel sound /ē/ as heard in **me** is spelled **ee.**
Take the Pretest.

Practice

A. Write these list words to answer the questions.

by	go	he	my	see	she	we

1. I am a word that tells what you do with your eyes. What word am I?

2. I am a word that means **next to**. What word am I?

3. I am a word that means the opposite of **come**. What word am I?

4. I am a word that means the opposite of **he**. What word am I?

5. I am a word that you might use when talking about something that is yours. What word am I?

6. I am a word that means the opposite of **she**. What word am I?

7. I am a word that means **you and I**. What word am I?

1. _____

2. _____

3. _____

4. _____

5. _____

6. _____

7. _____

B. Write these list words to complete the sentences.

be	me	so

I want to 1._____ a famous piano player, 2._____ I will practice very

hard. Then, people will come to hear 3._____ play.

Take the Check Test. Write on your Study Sheet the words you misspell.

Dictionary

A. Write these entry words in alphabetical order: **money, cake, bell, doll.**

1. _____ 2. _____ 3. _____ 4. _____

B. Write the correct entry words from above for the picture definitions.

1.

3.

2.

4.

1. _____ 2. _____ 3. _____ 4. _____

Spelling Challenge

fingers   keys   piano   <u>well</u>

Write the correct challenge words to complete the sentences.

1. Lee likes to play the _____ .

2. His ᵃ·_____ move swiftly over the ᵇ·_____ .

3. He plays very _____ .

Written Expression

A. Unscramble the words and write the sentences. Remember that each sentence must begin with a capital letter and end with a period.

1. week. birthday My last was

_____

2. me gave a Mom gift.

_____

3. gave a toy me She piano.

_____

B. Write one sentence that tells about the picture. Use at least one list word in the sentence.

_____

Take the Final Test.

boat   coat   feed   keep   soap

coal   eat   feet   read   week

Spelling Clues

Say each list word. Follow the directions.

A. Write the list words that have the following letters.

1. **oa**   a. _____   b. _____

c. _____   d. _____

2. **ea**   a. _____   b. _____

3. **ee**   a. _____   b. _____

c. _____   d. _____

B. Underline the correct answers. 1. The sound that the vowel letters stand for in each list word is called a **(long, short)** vowel sound. 2. Each list word contains **(one vowel letter, two vowel letters together)**.

A long vowel sound is often spelled with two vowel letters that are together as in **keep, eat,** and **coat.**

Take the Pretest.

Practice

A. Write the hidden list words below. Start with the first letter and write every letter except each **x.**

1. **exaxt**

- - - - - - - - - - - - - - - - -

2. **cxoxaxl**

- - - - - - - - - - - - - - - - -

3. **rxexaxd**

- - - - - - - - - - - - - - - -

4. **fxexext**

- - - - - - - - - - - - - - - - -

5. **fxexexd**

- - - - - - - - - - - - - - - - -

6. **kxexexp**

- - - - - - - - - - - - - - - - -

B. Write the list words that name the pictures.

1. _____
- - - - - - - - - - - - - - - -

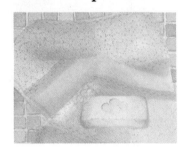

2. _____
- - - - - - - - - - - - - - - -

3. _____
- - - - - - - - - - - - - - - -

C. Write the list word that completes the sentence.

I am excited because I will start taking

_____

- - - - - - - - - - - - - - - -

music lessons next _____.

Take the Check Test. Write on your Study Sheet the words you misspell.

Word Building

Complete each sentence with two list words that rhyme.

1. I see a blue _____

in a red _____.

2. What animal can _____

with its _____?

3. Please _____

before you _____!

Spelling Challenge

perform   flute   music   will

Write the challenge words in the letter.

Dear Grandfather,

Please come to see me 1. _____ my 2. _____.

I 3. _____ play the 4. _____.

Love,
Sonja

Written Expression

Read each pair of words.

warm coat   red boat   hard coal   slick soap

The first word in each pair is a describing word.

The last word in each pair is a naming word.

A. Underline the describing word in each pair of words above. Circle the naming word in each pair of words.

B. Read the describing words that are beside each picture. Write the three words that describe each picture.

1.

brown   1. _____

new   _____

old   _____

shiny   _____

2.

white   2. _____

fluffy _____

hard   _____

soft   _____

3.

fat   3. _____

long   _____

silver _____

thin   _____

Take the Final Test.

day	say	away	stay	always
may	way	play	today	they

Spelling Clues

Say each list word. Follow the directions.

A. Write the list words that have the letters **ay**.

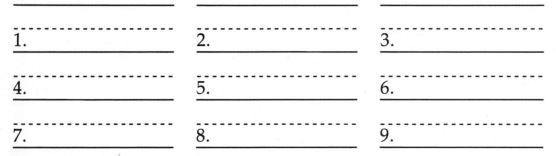

1. _____   2. _____   3. _____

4. _____   5. _____   6. _____

7. _____   8. _____   9. _____

B. Underline the correct answers. 1. The vowel sound in the list words you wrote is called a **(long, short)** vowel sound. 2. The letters that stand for this long vowel sound are **(a, a and y together, y)**.

> The long vowel sound /ā/ is sometimes spelled **ay** as in **day**.

Watch Out! Write the list word in which the long vowel

_____

sound /ā/ is not spelled **ay**. _____

Take the Pretest.

Practice

A. Write these list words to complete the story.

always away play stay they today

Grandfather and Grandmother live far 1._____ . I talked on

the telephone with them 2._____ . Grandmother said that

3._____ are coming to visit me. They are coming to hear me

4._____ my trumpet in the school band. They will 5._____

with me for one week. I wish they could 6._____ be here.

B. Change one letter in **hay** to form four list words. Write the words.

1._____ 2._____ 3._____ 4._____

Take the Check Test. Write on your Study Sheet the words you misspell.

Dictionary

A. Write **yes** beside each statement that is true.

_____ 1. The words listed in alphabetical order in a dictionary
_____   are called **entry words**.
_____

_____ 2. Each meaning in a dictionary is called a **definition**.
_____

B. Read the definitions below. Write one of the following words as the entry
word for each definition: **milk, coat, soap, boat.**
_____

1. _____ This is a small vessel for traveling on water.

2. _____ This is a piece of clothing worn to keep warm.

3. _____ This is a white liquid used for drinking and in cooking.

4. _____ This is a material used for washing things.

Spelling Challenge

band   brass   parade   color

Write the correct challenge words to complete the sentences.

1. A trumpet is made of a._____ and is the b._____
of gold.

2. All the bands marched in a _____ through the city.

3. A _____ is a group of people who play musical instruments.

Written Expression

Read each pair of words.

play   quietly   go   carefully   ran   eagerly   said   angrily

The first word in each pair shows action.
The last word in each pair tells how the action is or was done.

A. Underline the action word in each pair of words above. Circle the word that tells how the action is or was done.

B. Write two words from below each picture so that the set of sentences will tell about the picture.

happily   loudly   softly

_____
- - - - - - - - - - - - - - - - - - -

1. The children play _____ .
- - - - - - - - - - - - - - - - - - -
The children play _____ .

noisily   quietly   strongly

_____
- - - - - - - - - - - - - - - - - - -

2. The boy spoke _____ .
- - - - - - - - - - - - - - - - - - -
The boy spoke _____ .

quickly   merrily   sadly

_____
- - - - - - - - - - - - - - - - - - -

3. The children walked _____ .
- - - - - - - - - - - - - - - - - - -
The children walked _____ .

Take the Final Test.

baby	candy	story	many
pony	funny	any	only
very	happy	every	pretty

Spelling Clues

Say each list word. Follow the directions.

A. Write the list words.

1. _____   2. _____

3. _____   4. _____

5. _____   6. _____

7. _____   8. _____   9. _____

10. _____   11. _____   12. _____

B. Underline the correct answers. 1. The vowel sound at the end of each list word is called a **(long, short)** vowel sound. 2. The letter **(e, y, i)** stands for the long vowel sound at the end of each list word.

> The long vowel sound /ē/ at the end of a word is often spelled **y** as in **baby.**

Take the Pretest.

Practice

A. Write these list words to complete the poster.

every   funny   only

Enter the 1. _____ drum contest!

2. _____ person can enter!

The 3. _____ thing you need is a funny drum!

B. Write the list words that rhyme with the name of the picture.

1. _____

2. _____

C. Unscramble and write each list word from the drum.

1. _____

2. _____

3. _____

4. _____

5. _____

6. _____   7. _____

abyb   pypah   sotyr

nopy   teytrp   evyr   danyo

Take the Check Test. Write on your Study Sheet the words you misspell.

Word Building

Read each word. Circle the beginning consonant letter in each word. Change the beginning consonant letters to make the words that name the pictures. Write the words.

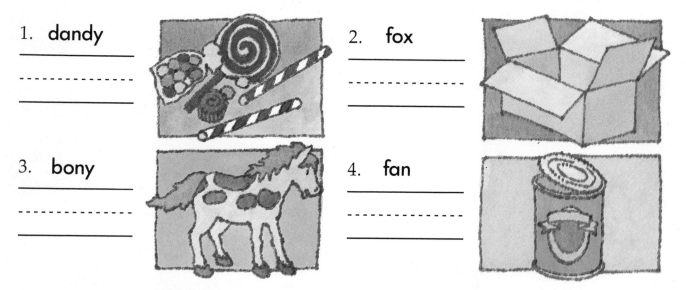

1. dandy

2. fox

3. bony

4. fan

Spelling Challenge

beat   drum   strike   done

Use the clues to write the challenge words in the puzzle. There is a mystery word in the yellow boxes.

1. hit
2. finished
3. rhythm
4. musical instrument played
with a stick

Write the mystery word. _____

Written Expression

A. Read each sentence. Circle the naming word in each sentence. Underline the describing word that tells about the naming word. Write the word you underlined below the sentence.

1. **I make happy music.**

_____

- - - - - - - - - - - - - - - - - - -

_____

2. **We saw a funny clown.**

_____

- - - - - - - - - - - - - - - - - - -

_____

3. **She makes a pretty sound.**

_____

- - - - - - - - - - - - - - - - - - -

_____

B. Read each sentence. Circle the word that shows action in each sentence. Underline the word that tells how the action is or was done. Write the word you underlined below the sentence.

1. **A triangle rings softly.**

_____

- -

_____

2. **The people danced happily.**

_____

- -

_____

Take the Final Test.

LESSON 16 Homophones

no	one	dear	hear	to
know	won	deer	here	too
				two

Spelling Clues

Say each list word. Follow the directions.

A. Write the sets of list words that sound the same.

1. a. _____ b. _____

2. a. _____ b. _____

3. a. _____ b. _____

4. a. _____ b. _____

5. a. _____ b. _____ c. _____

B. Underline the correct answers. 1. The words in each set above are spelled **(alike, differently)**. 2. The words in each set have **(the same, different)** meanings. 3. The words in each set sound **(alike, different)**.

> Some words sound alike or almost alike, such as **one** and **won**. Such words are called homophones. Homophones have different meanings, and they are spelled differently.

Take the Pretest.

Practice

A. Write **know** or **no** to complete each sentence.

1. Do you _____ how to play a harmonica?

2. _____ , but I would like to learn.

B. Write these list words to answer the questions.

dear   deer   hear   here   one   to   too   two   won

1. I am a word that names a wild animal. What word am I?

2. I am a word that means **also.** What word am I?

3. I am a word that is used at the opening of a letter. What word am I?

4. I am a word that is the same as the numeral **1.** What word am I?

5. I am a word that tells what you do with your ears. What word am I?

6. I am a word that is the same as the numeral **2.** What word am I?

7. I am a word that means the opposite of **lost.** What word am I?

8. I am a word that means **in this place.** What word am I?

9. I am a word that means **toward.** What word am I?

1. _____

2. _____

3. _____

4. _____

5. _____

6. _____

7. _____

8. _____

9. _____

Take the Check Test. Write on your Study Sheet the words you misspell.

Dictionary

A. Read each entry word and its sentence definition.

to   You must turn the wheel *to* the right.

too   I will go, *too*.

two   I have *two* dogs.

B. Write the homophones **to, too,** and **two** to complete the sentences.

1. I am going _____ the store.

2. I will spend my _____ dimes there.

3. You may go, _____ .

Spelling Challenge

voice   notes   songs   <u>mother</u>

Write the correct challenge words to complete the sentences.

   Do you know that you have a musical instrument called a

1. _____ ? You can use your voice to make music called

2. _____ . You can sing high or low 3. _____ .

Your father or 4. _____ can sing songs with you.

Review

Look at each word. If the word is spelled correctly, fill in the circle that has the letter **R.** If the word is misspelled, fill in the circle that has **Wr.** The first one has been done for you.

1. she ● (Wr)   12. storey (R) (Wr)

2. baby (R) (Wr)   13. thay (R) (Wr)

3. fien (R) (Wr)   14. kno (R) (Wr)

4. today (R) (Wr)   15. go (R) (Wr)

5. boet (R) (Wr)   16. won (R) (Wr)

6. wa (R) (Wr)   17. nise (R) (Wr)

7. coat (R) (Wr)   18. sta (R) (Wr)

8. day (R) (Wr)   19. feed (R) (Wr)

9. alwais (R) (Wr)   20. see (R) (Wr)

10. meny (R) (Wr)   21. ried (R) (Wr)

11. pony (R) (Wr)   22. read (R) (Wr)

Take the Final Test.

LESSON 17 Double Consonant Letters

apple	dinner	rabbit	daddy
kitten	summer	better	letter
supper	butter	little	yellow

Spelling Clues

Say each list word. Follow the directions.

A. Write the list words that have the following double letters.

1. **tt**   a. _____   b. _____   c. _____

   d. _____   e. _____

2. **bb** _____   3. **dd** _____

4. **pp**   a. _____   b. _____   5. **nn** _____

6. **mm** _____   7. **ll** _____

B. Underline the correct answers. 1. The double letters in each list word are **(consonant, vowel)** letters. 2. The double letters follow a **(vowel, consonant)** letter. 3. The sound that the vowel letter stands for is called a **(long, short)** vowel sound.

> A consonant sound that follows a short vowel sound is sometimes spelled with double consonant letters as in **apple.**

Take the Pretest.

Practice

A. Complete the sentences with list words from the box. Use the picture as a clue.

better
daddy
summer
yellow

1. My _____ uses a steamroller at work.

2. In the _____ the weather is very hot.

3. The _____ sun is hot and bright.

4. He feels _____ under an umbrella.

B. Use the picture clues to write the list words.

1. _____

2. _____

3. _____

4. _____

5. _____

C. Unscramble and write these list words.

1. **nnredi**

_____

2. **lttiel**

_____

3. **usppre**

_____

Take the Check Test. Write on your Study Sheet the words you misspell.

Dictionary

Write the words in alphabetical order. Read the sentences you write.

summer   kitten   likes   A

1. _____ .

banana   yellow   is   A

2. _____ .

butter   sweet   Apple   is

3. _____ .

Spelling Challenge

building   force   machines   <u>fine</u>

The sentences below tell about the pictures. Write
the correct challenge words to complete the sentences.

These pictures show 1._____ at work. The machines are

used for 2._____ . One machine will 3._____

stones to move. One machine is 4._____ for wrecking.

Written Expression

A. A describing word tells more about a naming word. Read the sentences below. Circle the words that describe the underlined words.
1. **That is a soft <u>kitten</u>.** 2. **We need hot <u>water</u>.**
3. **She is a happy <u>girl</u>.** 4. **I have a dry <u>towel</u>.**

B. Some words tell how an action is or was done. Underline the words that tell how the action was done in the sentences below. Write words from the truck that could be used in place of the underlined words.

1. The truck roared loudly. _____

2. The truck moved quickly. _____

3. The tires rolled softly. _____

4. The driver drove carefully. _____

C. Underline the describing word in this sentence: **That is a big tree.** Circle the words on the bricks that could be used in place of the word you underlined in the sentence.

<u>Take the Final Test.</u>

clean	black	close	stop
fly	place	glad	please
sled	sleep	still	flag

Spelling Clues

Say each list word. Follow the directions.

A. Write the list words that begin with the following letters.

1. **fl**   a. _____   b. _____

2. **sl**   a. _____   b. _____

3. **cl**   a. _____   b. _____

4. **pl**   a. _____   b. _____

5. **st**   a. _____   b. _____

6. **bl** _____   7. **gl** _____

B. Underline the correct answers. 1. The two letters that begin each list word are **(consonant, vowel)** letters. 2. The sounds of both letters **(can, cannot)** be heard when the words are said.

> A consonant blend is spelled with letters that stand for sounds you hear together, such as /fl/ spelled **fl** in **flag.**

Take the Pretest.

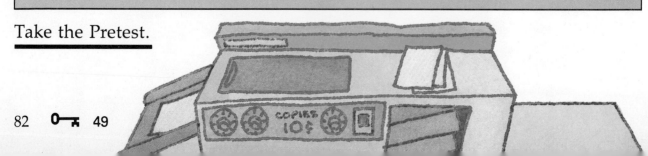

Practice

A. Look at the consonant blends on the typewriter keys. Write the blends in front of the letters on the paper to form list words.

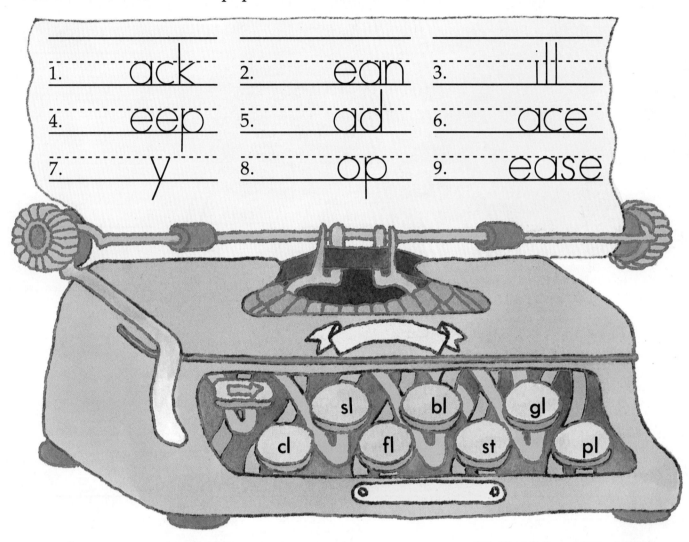

1. ____ ack   2. ____ ean   3. ____ ill
4. ____ eep   5. ____ ad   6. ____ ace
7. ____ y   8. ____ op   9. ____ ease

sl   bl   gl
cl   fl   st   pl

B. Draw a line through the word that does not make sense in each sentence below. Write a list word that does make sense in the sentence and that rhymes with the word you cross out.

1. We rode our said down the hill
of snow.

1. _____

2. The lag was red, white,
and blue.

2. _____

3. Please toes the door tightly.

3. _____

Take the Check Test. Write on your Study Sheet the words you misspell.

Word Building

Read the words on the first row of buttons of the telephone. Use the consonant blends to change the words to list words. Write the list words.

sack	bl +	ack
pop	st +	op
red	sl +	ed
bag	fl +	ag

1. _____

2. _____

3. _____

4. _____

Spelling Challenge

business   motor   telephone   hope

Write the correct challenge words after the clues.

1. helps a machine work

_____

2. a wish or dream

_____

3. someone's work

_____

4. used for talking to someone

_____

Written Expression

A. Sentences tell more when they have describing words in them. Read the pairs of sentences below. Underline the sentence in each pair that tells more.

1. It is a place.   It is a pretty place.

2. I have a clean office.   I have an office.

3. I saw a big flag.   I saw a flag.

B. Write each sentence below to tell how an action is or was done. Use one of the words on the adding machine tape in each sentence.

happily

quickly

brightly

1. She waved _____ .

2. Close the door _____ .

3. The sun shone _____ .

C. Write a sentence. Use a list word and one of these words: **softly, slowly, quietly.**

Take the Final Test.

bring	dress	brother	grass
friend	grade	from	drink
great	green	train	tree

Spelling Clues

Say each list word. Follow the directions.

A. Write the list words that begin with the following letters.

1. **br** a. _____ b. _____

2. **dr** a. _____ b. _____

3. **fr** a. _____ b. _____

4. **gr** a. _____ b. _____ c. _____

   d. _____ 5. **tr** a. _____ b. _____

B. Underline the correct answers. 1. Each list word begins with a **(consonant blend, vowel letter)**. 2. Each consonant sound in a consonant blend **(can, cannot)** be heard.

> A consonant blend is spelled with letters that stand for sounds you hear together, such as /br/ spelled **br** in **bring.**

Take the Pretest.

Practice

A. Complete the list words that name the pictures.

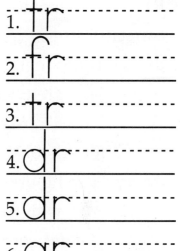

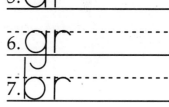

1. tr_____

2. fr_____

3. tr_____

4. dr_____

5. dr_____

6. gr_____

7. br_____

B. Write the correct list words below to complete the sentences.

grade   great   from   green   bring

1. "I will _____ a gift for you," Ana said.

2. Amy liked the gift she got _____ Ana.

3. Ana gave her a _____ notebook.

4. Amy and Ana are in the same _____ at school.

5. They are _____ friends.

Take the Check Test. Write on your Study Sheet the words you misspell.

Dictionary

Read each sentence. Write the numerals of the definitions beside the correct pictures.

dress 1. My friend had on a pretty *dress*.
2. I will *dress* for school.

drink 1. Bring me a *drink* with ice.
2. *Drink* some water from the glass.

train 1. The dog is on the *train*.
2. Did you *train* your dog to sit?

Spelling Challenge

hay   plow   tractor   <u>nice</u>

Write the correct challenge words to complete the sentences.

Farmers use a 1._____ to pull a 2._____ .

They stack or roll the 3._____ after cutting it. The golden hay

makes a 4._____ fall picture.

Written Expression

A. Read the letter that Rosa wrote to her brother David.

Dear David,
    I am having fun at the farm. I met a new friend. I help her do chores. She feeds hay to the horses. She gives the pigs water.
                    Love,
                    Rosa

1. Write the group of words from the letter that tells who the letter is for.

_____

- -

_____

This group of words in a letter is called the **greeting.**

2. Circle the capital **D** in the greeting of the letter above. The first word of a greeting always begins with a capital letter.

3. Circle the comma after **David** in the letter above. A comma follows the person's name in a greeting.

B. Read the letter David wrote back to Rosa.

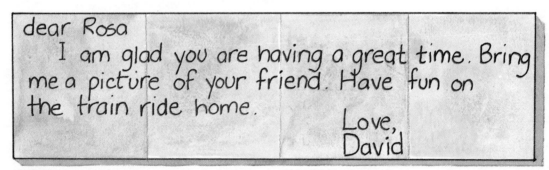

dear Rosa
    I am glad you are having a great time. Bring me a picture of your friend. Have fun on the train ride home.
                    Love,
                    David

1. Circle the mistakes David made in the greeting.

2. Write the greeting correctly.

_____

- -

_____

Take the Final Test.

LESSON 20 Spellings of /ch/, /sh/, and /w/

chair	children	church	where
sheep	show	when	what
while	white	why	<u>sure</u>

Spelling Clues

Say each list word. Follow the directions.

A. Write the list words that begin with the following consonant letters.

1. **wh** a. _____ b. _____ c. _____

   d. _____ e. _____ f. _____

2. **ch** a. _____ b. _____ c. _____

3. **sh** a. _____ b. _____

B. Underline the correct answer. The first two letters in each word you wrote stand for **(two, one)** sound(s).

> The sound /ch/ is usually spelled **ch** as at the beginning of **chair**. The sound /sh/ is usually spelled **sh** as at the beginning of **sheep**. The sound /w/ may be spelled **wh** as at the beginning of **when**.

Watch Out! Write the list word in which the beginning

_____

sound /sh/ is not spelled **sh**. _____
Take the Pretest.

Practice

Read the clues. Write the correct list words to reach the finish line.

1. rhymes with **kite**

2. is wooly and soft

3. rhymes with **sky**

4. young people

5. rhymes with **there**

6. a place of worship

7. rhymes with **know**

8. something to sit on

12. rhymes with **pile**

9. begins with **wh**; ends with **t**

10. /sh/ is spelled **s** in this word

11. begins with **wh**; ends with **n**

FINISH

Take the Check Test. Write on your Study Sheet the words you misspell.

Word Building

Draw a line through the words that do not make sense in the sentences below. Make new words that will make sense by changing the last letter of the words. Write the new words.

_____

1. The sheet are in the field. _____

2. Please shop me the picture. _____

3. The chain has four legs. _____

4. Who did you do that? _____

Spelling Challenge

automobile   travel   van   read

Write each challenge word in the picture it describes.

_____   _____

I like to 1._____ about places I can 2._____ to in

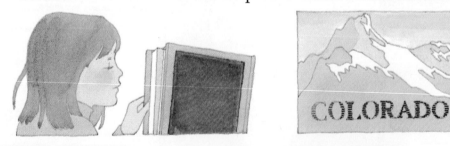

_____   _____

a 3._____ or in an 4._____ .

Written Expression

A. Read the letter Anita wrote to Sue.

> Dear Sue,
>   Where were you last week? What day did you come back from your travel? Did you ride in the new van?
>   Your friend,
>   Anita

1. Write the words Anita used to say good-by to Sue.

_____
- -
_____

This part of a letter is called the **closing.** The writer's name is written below the closing.

2. Circle the capital **Y** in the closing of Anita's letter. The first word of a closing always begins with a capital letter.

3. Circle the comma after **friend** in the letter. A comma always follows the last word in a closing.

B. Read the letter Sue wrote back to Anita.

> Dear Anita,
>   Last week we went to the beach. We took Kim's car instead of the travel van. We came back on Friday. We sure had a good time.
>   your friend
>   Sue

1. Circle the mistakes Sue made in the closing of her letter.

2. Write the closing in Sue's letter the way it should be written.

_____
- -
_____

Take the Final Test.

the	them	thank	think
than	then	these	their
that	this	thing	there

Spelling Clues

Say each list word. Follow the directions.

A. Write the list words.

1. _____
2. _____
3. _____
4. _____
5. _____
6. _____
7. _____
8. _____
9. _____
10. _____
11. _____
12. _____

B. Underline the correct answers. 1. The two letters that begin each list word are **(vowel, consonant)** letters. 2. The two letters stand for one **(vowel, consonant)** sound.

The sound /th/ is spelled **th** as in **than**. The sound /th/ is spelled **th** as in **think**.

Take the Pretest.

Practice

Form list words by adding the letters on the machines to the letters **th**. Cross out the letters as you use them. Use all the letters.

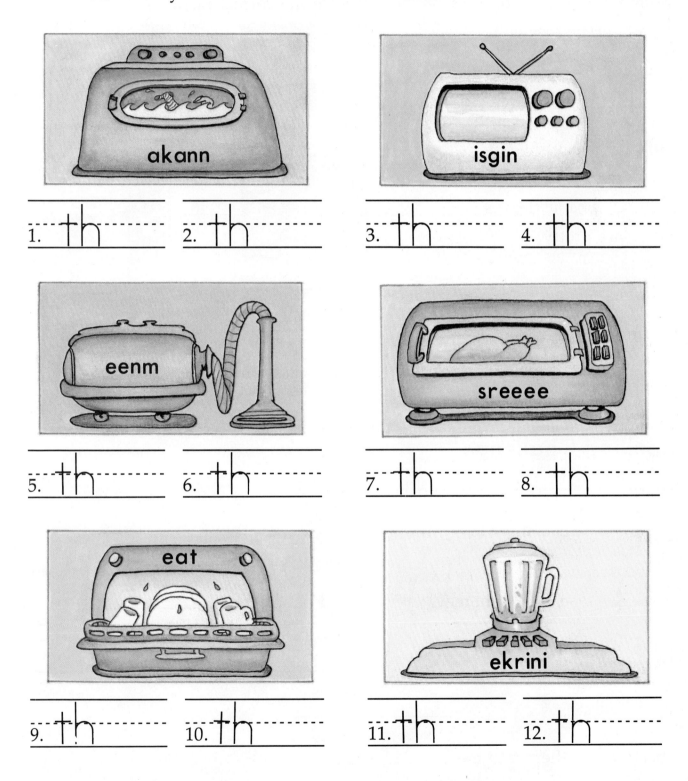

akann

isgin

1. th   2. th   3. th   4. th

eenm

sreeee

5. th   6. th   7. th   8. th

eat

ekrini

9. th   10. th   11. th   12. th

Take the Check Test. Write on your Study Sheet the words you misspell.

Dictionary

Write the numerals of the definitions beside the correct pictures.

cook 1. The *cook* will
prepare dinner.
2. I like to *cook!*

fall 1. The girl will
not *fall*.
2. The *fall* leaves
are pretty.

store 1. *Store* your toys
in a box.
2. He got a plane
at the toy *store*.

Spelling Challenge

dryer   stove   washer   <u>week</u>

Write the correct challenge words to complete the sentences.

We use machines at home. We cook food on the 1._____ .

Two days a 2._____ we clean clothes in the 3._____ .

Then we put them into the 4._____ .

Written Expression

A. Read the following letter.

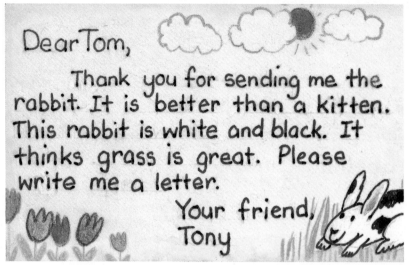

Dear Tom,

Thank you for sending me the rabbit. It is better than a kitten. This rabbit is white and black. It thinks grass is great. Please write me a letter.

Your friend,
Tony

Circle the capital letter that begins the greeting. Circle the comma that follows the greeting. Circle the capital letter that begins the closing. Circle the comma that follows the closing.

B. Write the letter above on the following lines.

_____

_____

_____

_____

_____

_____

_____

_____

_____

_____

_____

_____

Take the Final Test.

back	long	wish	sick
much	each	sing	with
fish	ring	teach	which

Spelling Clues

Say each list word. Follow the directions.

A. Write the list words that end with the following letters.

1. **ng** a. _____ b. _____ c. _____

2. **ch** a. _____ b. _____ c. _____

   d. _____

3. **ck** a. _____ b. _____

4. **th** _____ _____

5. **sh** a. _____ b. _____

B. Underline the correct answers. 1. The two letters that end each list word are (**vowel, consonant**) letters. 2. The two letters stand for (**one, two**) consonant sound(s).

> A single consonant sound at the end of a word is sometimes spelled with two consonant letters, such as /ng/ spelled **ng** in **ring.**

Take the Pretest.

Practice

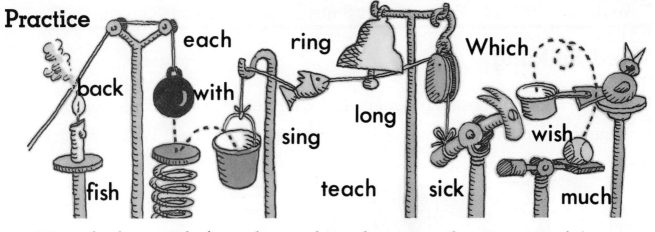

back
each
ring
with
Which
fish
sing
long
wish
teach
sick
much

A. Write the list words from the machine that mean the opposite of the words below.

1. front _____

2. healthy _____

3. short _____

4. learn _____

5. little _____

B. Write the correct list words from the machine to complete the sentences.

1. I _____ I could make the machine work.

2. I need to do _____ step carefully.

3. _____ part will I do first?

4. The _____ comes after the pail.

5. The fish will _____ the bell.

6. Will you work the machine _____ me?

7. If the machine works, the bird will _____ .

Take the Check Test. Write on your Study Sheet the words you misspell.

Word Building

Underline the two consonant letters at the end of each numbered word. Change these letters to form words that name the pictures. Write two list words that end with each pair of letters you write.

1. **sill**

sl   a. _____

b. _____

2. **crash**

cra   a. _____

b. _____

Spelling Challenge

cause   happens   unusual   **day**

Write the correct challenge words to complete the sentences.

This 1._____ machine is not like any other machine. Each

step will 2._____ the next step. It all 3._____

after the first step happens. One 4._____ it may really work!

Review

Read the words in each set. If one of the words is misspelled, fill in the numbered circle beside that word. If none of the words is misspelled, fill in the numbered circle beside the word **None**. The first one has been done for you.

A. ① apple
② flag
● dres
④ children
⑤ None

D. ① dady
② place
③ drink
④ while
⑤ None

G. ① better
② sleep
③ from
④ sure
⑤ None

B. ① dinner
② clen
③ grade
④ them
⑤ None

E. ① kitten
② fly
③ grass
④ thank
⑤ None

H. ① letter
② please
③ tran
④ think
⑤ None

C. ① little
② stil
③ tree
④ these
⑤ None

F. ① rabbit
② close
③ friend
④ each
⑤ None

I. ① sumer
② glad
③ great
④ fish
⑤ None

Take the Final Test.

cow	town	*cow*	*town*
how	about	*how*	*about*
now	brown	*now*	*brown*
our	found	*our*	*found*
out	around	*out*	*around*
down	house	*down*	*house*

Spelling Clues

Say each list word. Follow the directions.

A. Write the list words that have the letters **ow**.

1. _____ 2. _____ 3. _____

4. _____ 5. _____ 6. _____

B. Write the list words that have the letters **ou**.

1. _____ 2. _____ 3. _____

4. _____ 5. _____ 6. _____

C. Underline the pairs of letters that stand for the vowel sound /ou/ as heard in **out** in the list words you wrote above.

> The vowel sound /ou/ may be spelled **ou** as in **found** or **ow** as in **cow**.

Take the Pretest.

Practice

A. Write list words to complete the sentences about the pictures.

found
down
out
cow
brown

1.

1. She a._____ a b._____ lying c._____ .

2. Farmers dig a._____ potatoes b._____ of the ground.

B. Write the missing letters to complete the list words.

1. h_____   2. __r____   3. n_____   4. t_____

5. a_____t   6. a_____d   7. h__s__

Take the Check Test. Write on your Study Sheet the words you misspell.

Dictionary

a b c d e f g h i j k l m n o p q r s t u v w x y z

A. Write each group of words in alphabetical order. Look at the second letter of each word.

1.   it   in   is

2.   at   as   am

3.   oh   or   of

B. Write each group of words in alphabetical order. Look at the first and second letters of each word.

1.   go   us   up

2.   me   do   my

3.   by   we   be

Spelling Challenge

crop   field   ranches   <u>and</u>

Write the correct challenge words to complete the sentences.

1. Food comes from plants _____ animals.

2. Some beef comes from cattle raised on _____ .

3. The farmer planted wheat in the _____ .

4. Many people worked to pick a _____ of peaches.

Written Expression

A. Find the two mistakes in each date. Write each date correctly.

1. may 20 1982 _____

2. april 5 1981 _____

B. Find the two mistakes in each greeting. Write each greeting correctly.

1. dear jo, _____ 2. dear Al _____

C. Find the two mistakes in each closing. Write each closing correctly.

1. love _____ 2. sincerely _____

D. This friendly letter has twelve mistakes. Circle the mistakes. Use the activities above as clues.

march 10, 1981
dear Aunt sally
    Our class went to a farm
We walked around the barn.
a brown cow was in a stall.
We saw how the machine
milks her. I found eggs in the
chicken house We bent down
to see strawberries, then
we rode back to town
                love
                rhonda

Underline the nine list words in the letter. Circle the correct answer: The list words (**are, are not**) spelled correctly in the letter.

Take the Final Test.

LESSON 24 Spellings of /o͝o/

look	took	*look*	*took*
put	pull	*put*	*pull*
book	wood	*book*	*wood*
foot	would	*foot*	*would*
full	could	*full*	*could*
good	should	*good*	*should*

Spelling Clues

Say each list word. Follow the directions.

A. Write the list words in which /o͝o/ as heard in **book** is spelled with the following letters.

1. **oo**   a._____   b._____   c._____

    d._____   e._____   f._____

2. **ou**   a._____   b._____   c._____

B. Write the list words in which /o͝o/ is spelled with the single vowel letter **u**.

1._____   2._____   3._____

> The vowel sound /o͝o/ may be spelled **oo** as in **book**, **u** as in **full**, or **ou** as in **would**.

Take the Pretest.

Practice

A. Homophones are words that sound alike but have different meanings.

1. Underline the homophones **would** and **wood** in these sentences.

a. Jan would like to help.   b. She will bring the wood.

2. Write each homophone.

a. would _____   b. wood _____

B. Write these list words to complete the story.

book   could   foot   full   good   look   pull
put   took   should

Tom helped his dad 1._____ apples off the tree.

Tom put each 2._____ on a low branch so he 3._____

reach a higher branch. Tom and Dad 4._____ the apples home.

They peeled the apples and 5._____ them in a pot. Dad said,

"Now the directions say we 6._____ add water. Then we can

cook the apples." Tom read a 7._____ and waited. Sometimes

Dad would 8._____ in the pot to check the apples. Finally

Dad said, "Now we have enough 9._____ applesauce for two

10._____ jars."

Take the Check Test. Write on your Study Sheet the words you misspell.

Word Building

A. 1. Underline two rhyming list words in each sentence.

a. **The worker will put her foot on the machine.**

b. **The machine will pull the full box up the ramp.**

2. Write the rhyming words from the sentences above.

a. _____ b. _____ c. _____ d. _____

B. Write rhyming words. Put a consonant letter from each can in front of **ook**.

The first one has been done for you.

1. book   2. _____

3. _____   4. _____

Spelling Challenge

factory   freezing   package   too

Write the correct challenge words to complete the sentences.

1. Food is put in cans at a _____ .

2. Factory machines put food in boxes, _____ .

3. Machines put fish in a _____ .

4. Food can be kept fresh by _____ .

Written Expression

A. Read this friendly letter. Underline the **date, greeting,** and **closing.**

April 7, 1981

Dear Sam,
    I'm glad we could go to the bakery.
I liked to watch the bakers put full
pans in the oven. Here is the picture
I took.

               Love,
               George

B. Write a friendly letter to a person you know. Remember to use a date, a greeting, and a closing.

Take the Final Test.

LESSON 25 Spellings of /o͞o/

do	blue	*do*	*blue*
grew	room	*grew*	*room*
who	soon	*who*	*soon*
food	school	*food*	*school*
you	new	*you*	*new*
noon	knew	*noon*	*knew*

Spelling Clues

Say each list word. Follow the directions.

A. Write the list words that end with the letter **o**.

1. _____   2. _____

B. Write the list words that have the following letters.

1. **ew**   a. _____   b. _____   c. _____

2. **oo**   a. _____   b. _____   c. _____

        d. _____   e. _____

3. **ou** _____   4. **ue** _____

> The vowel sound /o͞o/ may be spelled **oo** as in **soon, ew** as in **new, o** as in **do, ou** as in **you,** or **ue** as in **blue.**

Take the Pretest.

Practice

A. 1. Underline the homophones **new** and **knew** in the following sentence.

I already knew how to ride my new bike.

2. Complete the sentence below with **knew** and **new.**

The a.＿＿＿＿＿＿ girl in school b.＿＿＿＿＿＿ how to add.

B. Find the list words hidden in the words below. Write the list words.

1. schoolyard ＿＿＿＿＿＿＿   2. bedroom ＿＿＿＿＿＿＿

3. doing ＿＿＿＿＿＿＿   4. whose ＿＿＿＿＿＿＿

5. afternoon ＿＿＿＿＿＿＿   6. bluebird ＿＿＿＿＿＿＿

C. Write list words to complete the sentences.

grew   food   soon   knew   you

1. The farmer ＿＿＿＿＿ the wheat.

2. The bakers ＿＿＿＿＿ how to make bread.

3. The truck drivers took the ＿＿＿＿＿ to the store.

4. People will buy the bread ＿＿＿＿＿ .

5. How would ＿＿＿＿＿ take the bread home?

Take the Check Test. Write on your Study Sheet the words you misspell.

Dictionary

a b c d e f g h i j k l m n o p q r s t u v w x y z

Write each set of letters in alphabetical order in front of the word parts.
Remember to look at the first and second letters. The first one has been done
for you.

1.

sm   so   st   sc   ____hool ____ile   ____on ____ay

school   ____ite   ____on   ____ay

2.

gl   ne   no   gr   ____ue ____ew   ____w ____on

____ue   ____ew   ____w   ____on

Spelling Challenge

carry   crate   deliver   came

Write the correct challenge words to complete the story.

A truck 1._____ to the store to

2._____ bananas. Workers will 3._____

each 4._____ of bananas off the truck.

Written Expression

A. Read this thank-you letter.

> May 5, 1981
>
> Dear Grandfather,
>
>   Thank you for the new blue lunchbox.
> I knew what to do with it. I took my
> lunch to school. We ate at noon.
>
>   Love,
>   Kathy

B. Copy the thank-you letter.

Take the Final Test.

or	for	*or*	*for*
corn	store	*corn*	*store*
door	four	*door*	*four*
more	yours	*more*	*yours*
horse	morning	*horse*	*morning*
your	before	*your*	*before*

Spelling Clues

Say each list word. Follow the directions.

A. Write the following list words: **for, corn, horse, morning.**

_____ _____ _____ _____

1. _____ 2. _____ 3. _____ 4. _____

Circle the letters that stand for /ôr/ as heard in **fork** in each word above.

B. Write the list words in which /ôr/ is spelled with the following letters.

1. **ore** a. _____ b. _____ c. _____

2. **our** a. _____ b. _____ c. _____

3. **oor** _____

> The sound /ôr/ may be spelled **or** as in **corn**, **ore** as in **more**, **oor** as in **door**, or **our** as in **your**.

Take the Pretest.

Practice

A. 1. Underline the homophones **four** and **for** in the following sentences.

a. The grocer has four peaches.   b. He will sell them for a dollar.

_____   _____

2. Write the homophones. 1. _____   2. _____

B. Write the list words that name the pictures.

_____   _____   _____   _____

1. _____   2. _____   3. _____   4. _____

C. Write list words to complete the grocery store signs.

1.

Start
_____
_____
day with
Vita-milk.

2.

Buy one box
and get one
_____
_____
box free!

3.

Buy the Giant
_____
_____
King size and
save money!

4.

Big sale starts
at 10:00 tomorrow
_____
_____

5.

Use this butter
_____ ___
_____ ___
_____ ___
May 29, 1985.

6.

Big sale!
A turkey
can be
_____
_____
_____

Take the Check Test. Write on your Study Sheet the words you misspell.

Word Building

Use the blue letters in place of the underlined letters to form new words from the list words. The first one has been done for you.

1. <u>c</u>orn   b   h   a. born   b. horn

2. cor<u>n</u>   k   d   a. _____   b. _____

3. <u>f</u>our   y   p   a. _____   b. _____

4. f<u>ou</u>r   ea   ai   a. _____   b. _____

5. f<u>o</u>r   u   a   a. _____   b. _____

6. s<u>t</u>ore   n   c   a. _____   b. _____

7. <u>m</u>ore   c   t   a. _____   b. _____

Spelling Challenge

cost   ad   shopping   <u>got</u>

A. Draw a line from each challenge word to its meaning.

1. cost   advertisement

2. ad   price

3. shopping   bought

4. got   looking at and buying things

B. Write the challenge words.

1. _____   2. _____   3. _____   4. _____

Written Expression

A. Find two mistakes in each date, greeting, closing, and sentence. Write the date, greeting, closing, and sentence correctly.

1. july 10 1981 _____

2. dear Joseph _____

3. love _____

4. I gave a hors more corn

_____

B. The thank-you letter below has twelve mistakes. Circle the mistakes.

> March 12 1981
>
> dear Aunt Betsy
>   thank you for the toy horse. The mail carrier left it at my door this morning. i played with it befor I went to the stor with my family. We bought four bags of food. I pretended to feed the horse some corn that we bought I like yowr gift very much
>
>   love,
>   tommy

Write correctly the three misspelled list words from the letter above.

1. _____   2. _____   3. _____

Take the Final Test.

LESSON 27 Spellings of /ûr/

her	heard	*her*	*heard*
bird	first	*bird*	*first*
hurt	work	*hurt*	*work*
turn	birthday	*turn*	*birthday*
third	fur	*third*	*fur*
girl	<u>were</u>	*girl*	*were*

Spelling Clues

Say each list word. Follow the directions.

Write the list words in which /ûr/ as heard in **fur** is spelled with the following letters.

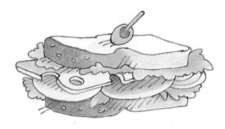

1. **ir**   a. _____   b. _____   c. _____

   d. _____   e. _____

2. **ur**   a. _____   b. _____   c. _____

3. **er** _____   4. **or** _____   5. **ear** _____

> The sound /ûr/ may be spelled **er** as in **her**, **ur** as in **fur**, **ir** as in **bird**, or as in **work**, or **ear** as in **heard**.

Watch Out!   Write **were**. _____   Circle the silent **e**.
Take the Pretest.

Practice

A. Write the list words to complete the sentences that tell about the picture.

1. The boy is _____ .

2. The _____ cake is second.

3. The _____ is _____ .

4. The _____ is fourth.

first
third
girl
bird
birthday

B. Write the hidden list words below. Start with the first letter and write every letter except each **x.** The first one has been done for you.

1. bxixrxd   *bird*

2. hxexaxrxd   _____

3. hxexr   _____

4. wxoxrxk   _____

5. hxuxrxt   _____

6. wxexrxe   _____

7. txuxrxn   _____

8. fxuxr   _____

9. gxixrxl   _____

10. txhxixrxd   _____

Take the Check Test. Write on your Study Sheet the words you misspell.

Dictionary

a b c d e f g h i j k l m n o p q r s t u v w x y z

Write each set of words in alphabetical order.

1. bird   bake
    boil   beat
    blend

2. fur   fork
    first feed
    fry

3. girl   sweet
    work   salty
    were

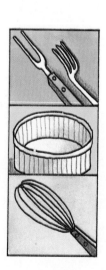

1. _____   2. _____   3. _____

Spelling Challenge

Write the correct challenge words to complete the sentences.

| crisp |
| knife |
| taste |
| can |

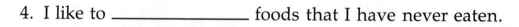

1. Fresh carrots and apples are _____ .

2. I use a _____ to cut potatoes.

3. We _____ cook food by boiling it.

4. I like to _____ foods that I have never eaten.

Written Expression

A. Read this thank-you letter. Circle the date, the greeting, and the closing.

March 26, 1982

Dear Dad,
   Thank you for the cookbook. The first thing I cooked was chicken soup. Then I made dinner for a friend. The food tasted good.
             Love,
             Andy

B. Write a thank-you letter. Remember to use a date, a greeting, and a closing.

Take the Final Test.

far	park	*far*	*park*
car	part	*car*	*part*
barn	large	*barn*	*large*
hard	party	*hard*	*party*
dark	garden	*dark*	*garden*
farm	<u>are</u>	*farm*	<u>*are*</u>

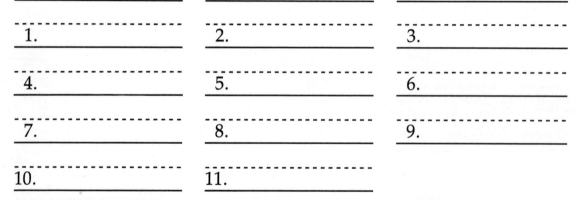

Spelling Clues

Say each list word. Follow the directions.

Write the first eleven list words.

1. _____

2. _____

3. _____

4. _____

5. _____

6. _____

7. _____

8. _____

9. _____

10. _____

11. _____

Underline the letters that stand for /är/ as heard in **car** in each list word you wrote.

> The sound /är/ is usually spelled **ar** as in **car.**

Watch Out! Write **are.** _____ Circle the silent **e.**
<u>Take the Pretest.</u>

Practice

A. Write the list words shown in the box to answer the questions.

| car |
| park |
| dark |
| large |
| barn |
| hard |
| garden |
| party |

1. What has four wheels and uses gas?

2. What building is a home for cows?

3. What is the opposite of **light?**

4. What is the opposite of **soft?**

5. Where is a good place to play baseball?

6. What is the opposite of **small?**

7. What might someone have on a birthday?

8. Where can people grow vegetables?

B. Read the scientists' reports below. Unscramble the underlined list words. Write the list words correctly.

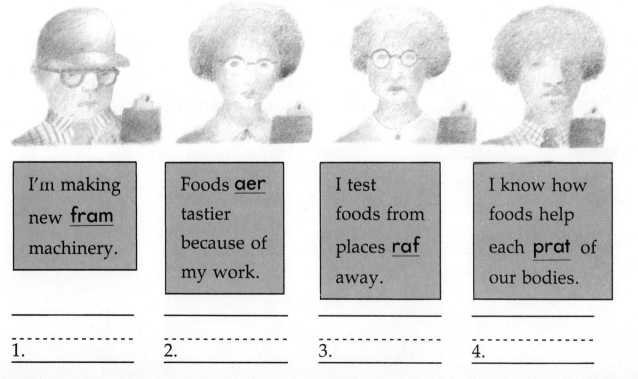

I'm making new **fram** machinery.

Foods **aer** tastier because of my work.

I test foods from places **raf** away.

I know how foods help each **prat** of our bodies.

1. _____

2. _____

3. _____

4. _____

Take the Check Test. Write on your Study Sheet the words you misspell.

Dictionary

Sometimes a dictionary has two or more entry words that have the same spelling. Each entry word is numbered. Read these dictionary entries.

seal[1]—The *seal* on my paper is gold.   **ring**[1]—I heard a bell *ring*.

seal[2]—We saw a *seal* at the zoo.   **ring**[2]—I wear a *ring* on my finger.

Write the entry words and numerals that go with the pictures.

1. _____   2. _____   3. _____   4. _____

Spelling Challenge

examine   expert   sample   play

Write each challenge word. Draw a line from each word you write to its clue.

_____

1. **play**   _____ to look at something very carefully

2. **expert**   _____ a person who knows something well

3. **sample**   _____ to have fun

4. **examine**   _____ a part of something

Review

Read the words in each set. If one of the words is misspelled, fill in the numbered circle beside that word. If none of the words is misspelled, fill in the numbered circle beside **none of these**. The first one has been done for you.

A. ① about
   ② blue
   ● brid
   ④ car
   ⑤ none of these

B. ① could
   ② knew
   ③ heard
   ④ garden
   ⑤ none of these

C. ① nou
   ② door
   ③ are
   ④ good
   ⑤ none of these

D. ① book
   ② befor
   ③ first
   ④ around
   ⑤ none of these

E. ① found
   ② noon
   ③ trun
   ④ your
   ⑤ none of these

F. ① look
   ② skool
   ③ dark
   ④ morning
   ⑤ none of these

G. ① brown
   ② fod
   ③ girl
   ④ hurt
   ⑤ none of these

H. ① foot
   ② corn
   ③ were
   ④ hous
   ⑤ none of these

I. ① out
   ② hors
   ③ farm
   ④ grew
   ⑤ none of these

Take the Final Test.

ever	sister	*ever*	*sister*
over	winter	*over*	*winter*
after	another	*after*	*another*
never	teacher	*never*	*teacher*
under	father	*under*	*father*
paper	picture	*paper*	*picture*

Spelling Clues

Say each list word. Follow the directions.

Write the list words in which the sound /ər/ as heard at the end of **after** is spelled **er**.

1. _____ 2. _____ 3. _____

4. _____ 5. _____ 6. _____

7. _____ 8. _____ 9. _____

10. _____ 11. _____

> The sound /ər/ is often spelled **er** as in **after**.

Watch Out! Write the list word in which the sound /ər/ as heard at the end

_____

of **after** is not spelled **er**. _____

Take the Pretest.

Practice

A. The underlined letters in the sentences below are scrambled list words. Unscramble the letters and write the list words. The first one has been done for you.

1. Have you **vree** heard of Paul Bunyan?

2. The **chaetre** read a book about him.

3. Paul found a baby ox one **ntrwie**.

4. It was **edrnu** the snow.

5. Paul named the ox Babe **ertfa** he saved it.

6. Babe was blue and **vrene** changed color.

7. One story said that Babe jumped **vero** a building.

8. In **eatnhor** story Babe drank a lake.

9. A **icpurte** showed that Babe the Blue Ox was a giant animal.

ever
_____
_____
_____
_____
_____
_____
_____
_____
_____

B. Write the list words that belong with the groups of words.

paper   father   sister
_____

1. girl, woman, _____

2. man, dad, _____

3. pen, pencil, _____

Take the Check Test. Write on your Study Sheet the words you misspell.

Dictionary

a b c d e f g h i j k l m n o p q r s t u v w x y z

Write each group of words below in alphabetical order. Each group of words will form a sentence. Remember to write a period at the end of the sentence.

1. found paper Fran's Father

2. over Look picture Paul's

3. lunch After sister started Lynn's swinging

Spelling Challenge

Write the correct challenge words to answer the questions.

| giant |
| strength |
| tales |
| he |

1. What are some stories called?

2. Which word means **very big?**

3. Which word means the opposite of **she?**

4. What helped Babe pull heavy logs?

1. _____

2. _____

3. _____

4. _____

Written Expression

A. Read the poem below. Complete the last verse of the poem by writing a list word that rhymes with **bother.**

Babe the Blue Ox

Out one winter Paul Bunyan did go
And found a blue ox under the snow.
Where was its mother? Paul didn't know.
Paul called him Babe, saying, "I'll help you grow."

Babe was blue, the biggest ox ever.
When he walked, trees shook like a feather.
Just swinging his tail could change the weather.
Though some people say, "Not true! No! Never!"

Old Babe could eat and eat like no other.
He ate one pasture, then cried, "Another!"
The farmer said, "Babe's not a bother.
_____
I only hope I don't meet his _____."

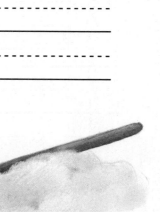

B. Write the words from the poem above that rhyme with the words below.

1. go, know   a._____   b._____

2. feather, weather   a._____   b._____

3. other   _____

Take the Final Test.

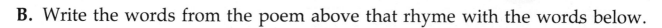

all	call	*all*	*call*
dog	fall	*dog*	*fall*
saw	water	*saw*	*water*
also	walk	*also*	*walk*
ball	because	*ball*	*because*
off	thought	*off*	*thought*

Spelling Clues

Say each list word. Follow the directions.

Write the list words in which /ô/ as heard in **saw** is spelled with the following letters.

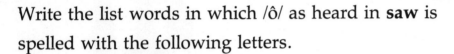

1. **aw** _____ 2. **o** a. _____ b. _____

3. **au** _____ 4. **ou** _____

5. **a followed by 1** a. _____ b. _____ c. _____

d. _____ e. _____ f. _____

6. **a after w** a. _____ b. _____

> The vowel sound /ô/ may be spelled **a** as in **all** and **water**, **au** as in **because**, **aw** as in **saw**, **o** as in **dog**, or **ou** as in **thought**.

Take the Pretest.

Practice

A. Read the story. Unscramble and write the underlined list words below the story.

A long time ago people believed the world was flat. They **thghotu** ships that sailed too far might **flla fof** the edge. People **soal** thought that dragons lived in the ocean **warte** near the edge of the world. They believed that dragons lived on land, too. People thought that dragons could swim, fly, and **wlka,** and that **lla** dragons could blow fire out of their noses. Many people were afraid of dragons **caubese** they thought dragons were terrible monsters. Many people believed in dragons, but nobody ever really **asw** one.

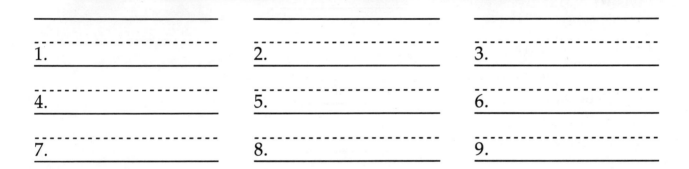

1. _____	2. _____	3. _____
4. _____	5. _____	6. _____
7. _____	8. _____	9. _____

B. Write the list words that go with the pictures.

1. _____   2. _____   3. _____

Take the Check Test. Write on your Study Sheet the words you misspell.

Dictionary

Sometimes a dictionary has two or more entry words that have the same spelling. Each entry word is numbered. Read these dictionary entries.

ball[1]—I can catch a *ball*.

ball[2]—Cinderella went to a *ball*.

bill[1]—She paid the *bill*.

bill[2]—A duck's *bill* is flat.

fly[1]—Airplanes can *fly*.

fly[2]—A *fly* is an insect.

saw[1]—A *saw* will cut the board.

saw[2]—She *saw* that movie.

Write the entry words and numerals for the meanings of the underlined words in the sentences below. The first one has been done for you.

1. She can hit a <u>ball.</u>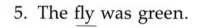

2. I wish I could <u>fly</u>.

3. The <u>bill</u> was $5.00.

4. We never <u>saw</u> a dragon.

5. The <u>fly</u> was green.

Spelling Challenge

dragon   fierce   save   <u>any</u>

Write the challenge words beside the correct meanings.

1. a monster _____   2. help; rescue _____

3. one; some _____   4. mean; cruel _____

Written Expression

Write the list words shown in the box to complete the poem.

Brenda the Dragon

water	dog
call	walk
ball	

Brenda, a dragon living in a lake,
Woke up saying, "Oh, for goodness sake!
It's my birthday and there's nothing at all!

Not even cards or a telephone 1. _____ !"

"Oh, rats!" cried the mighty dragon daughter

As she splashed her tail hard on the 2. _____ .
Then she blew fire for two miles around,
Warming the air with a loud, snapping sound.

"Hey, now!" barked a voice from behind a log.

Brenda looked up and saw a big red 3. _____ .
"Don't be crying all those tears," she did say.
"There's no time for that, not on your birthday."

So surprised Brenda was, her chin did fall.

For here came the red dog rolling a 4. _____ .
"It's a present for you," the dog did talk.

"Now dry your eyes and let's go for a 5. _____ ."
Take the Final Test.

LESSON 31 Compound Words

into	football	*into*	*football*
upon	something	*upon*	*something*
forget	sometimes	*forget*	*sometimes*
outside	grandfather	*outside*	*grandfather*
anything	grandmother	*anything*	*grandmother*
airplane	everyone	*airplane*	*everyone*

Spelling Clues

Say each list word. Follow the directions.

Write the list words that are formed from the following words.

1. for get _____

2. foot ball _____

3. out side _____

4. in to _____

5. every one _____

6. up on _____

7. air plane _____

8. any thing _____

9. grand mother _____

10. some times _____

Two or more words can be put together to make a compound word, such as **football**.

Take the Pretest.

134

Practice

Follow the directions to move up and down the game board. Write the words you land on. Start on **Go.**

GO
into
anything
upon
football
forget
sometimes
airplane
grandfather
outside
everyone
something
grandmother

_____

1. Jump ahead 4 spaces. _____

2. Jump ahead 3 spaces. _____

3. Jump ahead 5 spaces. _____

4. Jump back 2 spaces. _____

5. Jump back 4 spaces. _____

6. Jump back 3 spaces. _____

7. Jump back 1 space. _____

8. Jump ahead 3 spaces. _____

9. Jump back 4 spaces. _____

10. Jump ahead 7 spaces. _____

11. Jump ahead 3 spaces. _____

12. Jump back 2 spaces. _____

Take the Check Test. Write on your Study Sheet the words you misspell.

Word Building

A. A compound word is two or more words spelled together. Write the two words that form each compound word below.

1. sometimes _____ _____

2. everyone _____ _____

3. anything _____ _____

B. Draw a line from each word in the first column to a word in the second column to form compound list words. Write the compound words.

1. some   father   _____

2. grand   thing   _____

Spelling Challenge

Write the challenge words that go with the pictures.

bridle   flew   galloping   him

1. _____

2. _____

3. _____

4. _____

1.

2.

3.

4.

Written Expression

A. Complete these sentences about the make-believe picture. Use the list words shown in the box.

| outside |
| football |
| everyone |

1. Pegasus played with a _____ .

2. He asked _____ to play with him.

3. They played football _____ on the grass.

B. Complete these sentences about the real picture. Use the list words shown in the box.

| airplane |
| sometimes |
| grandfather |

1. My _____ likes to fly.

2. He flies an _____ .

3. I fly with him _____ .

Take the Final Test.

137

boys	lots	*boys*	*lots*
girls	nuts	*girls*	*nuts*
cars	books	*cars*	*books*
days	dolls	*days*	*dolls*
eggs	things	*eggs*	*things*
years	friends	*years*	*friends*

Spelling Clues

Say each list word. Follow the directions.

A. Write the list words that are forms of the words below.

1. boy _____

2. book _____

3. egg _____

4. year _____

5. girl _____

6. friend _____

7. nut _____

8. thing _____

9. car _____

10. doll _____

11. day _____

12. lot _____

B. Circle the correct answer. Each list word names (**one, more than one**).

> Words that name more than one usually end with **s** as in **books**.

Take the Pretest.

Practice

A. Write these list words to name the pictures: **dolls, girls, boys, cars.**

1. _____   2. _____   3. _____   4. _____

B. Each word below names one of something. Beside each word write the list word that names more than one. The first one has been done for you.

1. **doll** dolls

2. **nut** _____

3. **lot** _____

4. **thing** _____

5. **day** _____

6. **year** _____

C. Write the list words to complete the sentences: **books, years, friends, eggs.**

1. My _____ like stories about the phoenix.

2. They read about the phoenix in _____ .

3. Each phoenix lived 500 _____ .

4. It did not lay _____ .

139

Take the Check Test. Write on your Study Sheet the words you misspell.

Word Building

Write words that name more than one by adding **s** to the words that are on the phoenix's feathers.

1. book
2. car
3. doll
4. thing
5. friend
6. year

1. _____

2. _____

3. _____

4. _____

5. _____

6. _____

Spelling Challenge

ashes   eagle   flames   many

Write the correct challenge words to complete the sentences.

1. The phoenix was larger than an _____ .

2. It lived for _____ years.

3. Then it burned itself in _____ .

4. A new phoenix rose out of the _____ .

Written Expression

A. Underline the pictures that show something make-believe.

B. Write the correct words so that the sentences will tell about something make-believe.

read books about; ride for days on

1. People _____ the phoenix.

dragons with dolls; toy cars and dolls

2. They saw _____ .

C. Write the words that make the sentences tell about something real.

do many things; fly away on Pegasus

1. I can _____ .

phoenix eggs; nuts and eggs

2. People eat _____ .

Take the Final Test.

LESSON 33 The Ending Spelled *ed*

played	looked	*played*	*looked*
asked	wanted	*asked*	*wanted*
called	liked	*called*	*liked*
helped	lived	*helped*	*lived*
started	named	*started*	*named*
jumped	used	*jumped*	*used*

Spelling Clues

Say each list word. Follow the directions.

A. Write the list words that are formed from the following words.

1. ask   2. look   3. want   4. jump   5. play   6. call

1. _____   2. _____   3. _____

4. _____   5. _____   6. _____

Underline the last two letters of each list word you wrote.

B. Write the list words that are formed
from the following words.

1. like   2. use   3. name   4. live

1. _____   2. _____

3. _____   4. _____

Write the letter that was dropped from each word before **ed** was added. ____

> The ending spelled **ed** is sometimes added to words as in **asked** and **liked**.

Take the Pretest.

142

Practice

A. Use the underlined letters in the words below and the letters in the boxes to write list words. The first one has been done for you.

1. w̲ a̲ t̲ c h e̲ d̲ | n |
2. a̲ c t e̲ d̲ | sk |
3. h̲ e̲ l̲ d̲ | pe |
4. c o̲ o̲ k e d | l |
5. h i̲ k̲ e d | l |
6. p̲ l̲ a̲ c e̲ d | y |
7. g a̲ m̲ e | nd |
8. c̲ r a̲ w l̲ e̲ d̲ | l |
9. l̲ o v̲ e̲ d̲ | i |

1. wanted
2. _____
3. _____
4. _____
5. _____
6. _____
7. _____
8. _____
9. _____

B. Complete the sentences by writing the list words formed from the words on the left.

use 1. Some Indians _____ the thunderbird to explain thunder and lightning.

start 2. The thunderbird _____ thunder by beating its wings.

jump 3. Lightning _____ from the thunderbird's mouth.

143

Take the Check Test. Write on your Study Sheet the words you misspell.

Word Building

Write the list words formed from the words below.

If a word ends with **e**, drop the **e** and then add **ed.**

1. jump

2. start

3. live

4. play

5. like

6. call

Spelling Challenge

Unscramble the letters. Write the challenge words.

| believed |
| lightning |
| thunder |
| <u>now</u> |

1. lghiintng

2. onw

3. lebevied

4. tnheudr

Written Expression

A. Write a sentence about this make-believe picture.

_____

B. Write a sentence about this real picture.

_____

C. Write a sentence that tells something real about you.

_____

D. Write a sentence that tells something make-believe about you.

_____

Take the Final Test.

doing	looking	*doing*	*looking*
playing	working	*playing*	*working*
going	spelling	*going*	*spelling*
eating	coming	*eating*	*coming*
fishing	getting	*fishing*	*getting*
reading	making	*reading*	*making*

Spelling Clues

Say each list word. Follow the directions.

A. Write the list words that are formed from these words.
1. eat   2. go   3. work   4. fish   5. play   6. spell   7. do
8. look   9. read

1. _____   2. _____   3. _____

4. _____   5. _____   6. _____

7. _____   8. _____   9. _____

Underline the last three letters of each word you wrote.

B. Write the list words formed from these words. 1. come   2. make   3. get

1. _____   2. _____   3. _____

> The ending spelled **ing** is sometimes added to words as in **doing, coming,** and **getting.**

Take the Pretest.

Practice

A. Write the list word formed from each underlined word.

1. Cora likes to **play**. She is _____ in the sand.

2. Lynn went to **fish**. She took her _____ pole.

3. Do you like to **read**? What do you enjoy _____?

4. Mario came to **eat** lunch with us. We are _____ stew.

5. Sue can **look** at things carefully. She is _____ at bugs.

6. Ron tries to **spell** well. He studies the _____ words.

B. Complete the sentences by writing the list words formed from the words on the left.

do   1. What are you _____?

work   2. I am _____.

make   3. I am _____ a unicorn.

go   4. Are you _____ to sell it?

come   5. A woman is _____ to buy it.

get   6. She is _____ it for her son.

Take the Check Test. Write on your Study Sheet the words you misspell.

Word Building

A. Write the words formed by adding **ing** to each word.

1. read _____   2. eat _____

3. fish _____   4. work _____

B. Write the words formed by dropping the final letter **e** and adding **ing** to each word.

1. come _____   2. make _____

3. name _____   4. live _____

C. Write the words formed by doubling the final consonant letter and adding **ing** to each word.

1. get _____   2. put _____

3. run _____

Spelling Challenge

Write the correct challenge words to complete the sentences.

| horn |
| middle |
| twist |
| know |

Do you 1._____ about the unicorn? The unicorn

has one 2._____ in the 3._____

of its head. The horn has a 4._____ in it.

Review

Read the words in each set. If one of the words is misspelled, fill in the numbered circle beside that word. If none of the words is misspelled, fill in the numbered circle beside the word **None**. The first one has been done for you.

A. ● aftr
   ② fall
   ③ sometimes
   ④ nuts
   ⑤ None

D. ① another
   ② airplan
   ③ books
   ④ asked
   ⑤ None

G. ① all
   ② off
   ③ days
   ④ comeing
   ⑤ None

B. ① anything
   ② doing
   ③ calld
   ④ father
   ⑤ None

E. ① jumped
   ② boys
   ③ spelling
   ④ allso
   ⑤ None

H. ① fishing
   ② liked
   ③ thot
   ④ never
   ⑤ None

C. ① paper
   ② walk
   ③ dolls
   ④ things
   ⑤ None

F. ① because
   ② geting
   ③ named
   ④ everyone
   ⑤ None

I. ① picture
   ② football
   ③ lookt
   ④ making
   ⑤ None

Take the Final Test.

KEY CHART

VOWEL SPELLINGS

Key Sound	Spellings
1 /ā/	ate, cake
	day
2 /ē/	feet, tree
	eat, leaf, tea
	me
	lazy
3 /ī/	ice, ride
	my
4 /ō/	rope
	oak, coat
	no
5 /ū/	use, mule
6 /ă/	am, cat, fast
7 /ĕ/	end, bed, help
8 /ĭ/	it, pig, milk
9 /ŏ/	on, top, pond
10 /ŭ/	up, cup, jump
	oven, won, mother
11 /ô/	author, fault
	all, talk (before
	ll or lk)
	saw
12 /oi/	toy
13 /o͞o/	moon, zoo
	whom, do
	chew
	blue
14 /o͝o/	book
	push
	could
15 /ou/	out, round
	cow, owl, down
	(end of word;
	before single
	1 or n)
16 /ə/	parade, elevator
	cabinet, occur
	circus

VOWEL SPELLINGS WITH *R*

Key Sound	Spellings
17 /är/	art, car
18 /âr/	air, chair
19 /ĭr/	ear, clear
	cheer
20 /ôr/	or, corn, for
	store
21 /ûr/	fern, her
	bird, stir
	turn, fur
	earth, learn
	worm (after w)
22 /ər/	dollar, paper,
	doctor

CONSONANT SPELLINGS

	Key Sound	Spellings
23	/b/	boat, web, bubble
24	/ch/	chain, which
25	/d/	dog, red, middle
26	/f/	fish, roof, waffle
27	/g/	gate, flag, beggar
28	/h/	hat
		who
29	/j/	jump
		page
30	/k/	key, kite, look (before e or i)
		cat, coat, cup (before a, o, u)
		truck, ticket (after a short vowel sound)
31	/ks/	box, next
32	/kw/	queen
33	/l/	leaf, sail, hello
34	/m/	man, am, summer
35	/n/	nut, pin, penny
		know
36	/ng/	ring
		bank, angry (before /k/ or /g/)
37	/p/	pet, stop, suppose
38	/r/	run, for, carry
39	/s/	sun, bus, message
		house
		race
40	/sh/	shop, wish
41	/t/	toy, pet, little
42	/th/	think, path
43	/th/	this, bathe, other
44	/v/	vase
		have
45	/w/	wood
		white
46	/y/	yarn
47	/z/	zoo, quiz, puzzle
		was, reason
		cause
48	/zh/	measure
		television

CONSONANT BLENDS WITH THE SOUND /k/

49   close, cry, scare, school skip, scream, square

FINAL DOUBLE CONSONANT LETTERS

50   add, puff, egg, bell, inn, purr, glass, mitt, buzz

SPELLING DICTIONARY

A a

ashes (ash es)
The gray powder that is left after something has been burned is *ashes*.

automobile (au to mo bile)
A car is an *automobile*.

B b

back (back)
1. I sleep on my *back*.
2. When will you be *back*?

barn (barn)
A farm building for storing hay and animals is a *barn*.

because (be cause)
I cannot go *because* I am sick.

been (been)
I have *been* there before.

bill[1] (bill)
The cost of the toy was written on the *bill*.

bill[2] (bill)
A duck's mouth is called a *bill*.

blue (blue)
On a clear day the color of the sky is *blue*.

bow[1] (bow)
I bend over when I take a *bow*.

bow[2] (bow)
1. A knot with loops in it is a *bow*.
2. I use a *bow* to play my violin.

brass (brass)
The yellow metal from which trumpets are made is *brass*.

bridle (bri dle)
She put the *bridle* on the horse's head.

C c

can[1] (can)
Pablo *can* go with you.

can[2] (can)
The food was stored in the metal *can*.

coal (coal)

A black mineral that can be burned for heat is *coal*.

color (col or)

Blue is my favorite *color*.

coming (com ing)

They are *coming* to Texas next week.

crate (crate)

A wooden box used for packing things is a *crate*.

crisp (crisp)

Something dry and easily broken is *crisp*.

crop (crop)

Anything grown on a farm is a *crop*.

D d

dear (dear)

My friend is a *dear* person.

deer (deer)

A *deer* is a graceful wild animal.

deliver (de liv er)

When people carry and give letters to me, they *deliver* the letters.

does (does)

Beth *does* her job well.

E e

eagle (ea gle)

A large bird with strong wings and good eyes is an *eagle*.

every (eve ry)

I can read *every* story in the book.

examine (ex am ine)

The doctor will look carefully at my finger to *examine* it.

expert (ex pert)

A person who knows a lot about cats is an *expert* on cats.

F f

far (far)

Something that is a great distance away is *far* away.

feet (feet)

1. The parts of the body at the ends of the legs are *feet*.

2. Measures of length that are each equal to twelve inches are *feet*.

fierce (fierce)

Something that is frightening and mean is *fierce*.

flames (flames)

He could see the red and yellow *flames* of the fire.

flute (flute)

Carla played her long, thin *flute* to make music.

football (foot ball)

An oval ball pointed at both ends is a *football*.

for (for)

I worked on it *for* two days.

four (four)

One more than three is *four*.

friend (friend)

A person who likes me and helps me is my *friend*.

fur (fur)

The soft hair on many animals is called *fur*.

G g

galloping (gal lop ing)

When a horse is running fast, it is *galloping*.

give (give)

The teacher will *give* me the box.

grain (grain)

A small, hard seed from a plant such as wheat is a *grain*.

great (great)

Something very large or very important is something *great*.

H h

harp (harp)

I play the strings of a *harp* with my fingers to make music.

have (have)

I *have* a cat.

hear (hear)

When I listen to a sound with my ears, I can *hear* the sound.

here (here)

We'll eat *here*, in this place.

hill (hill)

A high piece of ground that is lower than a mountain is a *hill*.

hobby (hob by)

Something a person does for fun is a *hobby*.

hoe (hoe)

A garden tool with a flat blade across the end of a long handle is a *hoe*.

hummingbird (hum ming bird)

A tiny, brightly-colored bird with a long bill is a *hummingbird*.

J j

job (job)

My mother has a *job* working with that company.

K k

kite (kite)

My *kite* of paper and wood has a long string for flying.

knew (knew)

The pupils *knew* the lesson well.

know (know)

Sarah and Carlos *know* about cars.

L l

lived (lived)

Last year our neighbors *lived* in New York.

M m

many (many)

A school has room for *many* children.

motor (mo tor)

The machine that makes a car run is a *motor*.

N n

named (named)

1. They *named* their baby Paul.
2. Mrs. Wallace was *named* coach.

new (new)

The *new* table in our classroom has never been used.

no (no)

No, the dog is not sick.

noon (noon)

Charles ate lunch at 12:00, which is *noon.*

now (now)

I have to go *now,* at this time.

O o

of (of)

The boat is made *of* wood.

once (once)

I eat lunch *once* each day.

one (one)

Every person has *one* nose.

only (on ly)

We have *only* one teacher.

P p

park (park)

1. A beautiful piece of land where anyone can walk or play is a *park.*
2. When someone leaves a car in one place for a time, they *park* the car.

pet (pet)

1. A tame animal kept to play with is a *pet.*
2. Pat an animal softly to *pet* it.

picture (pic ture)

A painting is a *picture.*

plow (plow)

A large tool used by farmers to turn over soil is a *plow.*

pretty (pret ty)

Something that is beautiful is *pretty.*

R r

ring[1] (ring)

I heard a bell *ring*.

ring[2] (ring)

I wear a *ring* on my finger.

S s

said (said)

"Yes," the teacher *said*.

same (same)

Things that are alike are the *same*.

says (says)

Julie *says* she will go.

set (set)

1. Marie *set* the box on the table.
2. The *set* of dishes is blue.

sheep (sheep)

An animal that eats grass and is covered with wool is a *sheep*.

should (should)

You *should* do your homework.

sled (sled)

A thing with runners used for carrying people over snow is a *sled*.

soap (soap)

Use *soap* for washing your hands.

started (start ed)

When the light turned green, the bus *started* to move.

still (still)

1. The cat sat very *still*, without moving or making any noise.
2. Snow is *still* falling.

strength (strength)

Something that is strong has *strength*.

summer (sum mer)

The warmest days of the year are in the *summer*.

supper (sup per)

An evening meal may be called *supper*.

sure (sure)

I am *sure* the store is open.

T t

tales (tales)
Stories are *tales*.

their (their)
The children are eating *their* lunches.

there (there)
The bag is *there*, in that place.

they (they)
I know when *they* are coming.

to (to)
1. All the children went *to* school.
2. This is the key *to* the car.

too (too)
1. The neighbors are going, *too*.
2. The water is *too* hot.

town (town)
A small city is a *town*.

train (train)
1. A line of railroad cars hooked together is a *train*.
2. My dog will learn tricks if I *train* it.

turn (turn)
1. When I *turn*, I move around to face another direction.
2. It's your *turn* to be the leader.

two (two)
A rabbit has *two* long ears.

U u

until (un til)
We waited *until* nine o'clock.

unusual (un u su al)
Something that is not usual is *unusual*.

used (used)
1. The children *used* the paint.
2. They sell *used* cars.

V v

van (van)
A covered truck for moving people or things is a *van*.

W w

walk (walk)

I *walk* to school.

want (want)

Do you *want* to play outside?

was (was)

Tina *was* here yesterday.

week (week)

A *week* is seven days.

well[1] (well)

A hole dug in the ground for water is a *well*.

well[2] (well)

1. Doing something in a good way is doing it *well*.
2. Being in good health is being *well*.

were (were)

We *were* there all day.

what (what)

Do you know *what* to bring?

where (where)

I know the place *where* it happened.

winter (win ter)

The coldest days of the year are in the *winter*.

won (won)

Our team *won* the game.

wood (wood)

The hard part under the bark of a tree is *wood*.

would (would)

I *would* like to do it.

Aa Bb Cc Dd

Ee Ff Gg Hh

Ii Jj Kk Ll

Mm Nn Oo Pp

Qq Rr Ss Tt

Uu Vv Ww Xx

Yy Zz

2 3 4 5 6 7 8 9 10—89 88 87 86 85 84 83 82 81